MW00668648

Rich Hill

The History of
Arizona's Most Amazing
Gold District

M. Katherine Crombie, Ph.D.
Chris T. Gholson, B.S.
Dante S. Lauretta, Ph.D.
Erik B. Melchiorre, Ph.D.

Cataloging-in-Publication Data

Crombie, M. Katherine.
    Rich Hill : the history of Arizona's most amazing gold district / M. Katherine
    Crombie ... [et al.].
    Tuscon, Ariz. : Golden Retriever Publications, 2002.
    252 p. : ill. ; 15 x 25 cm.
    Includes bibliographical references and index.
    ISBN 0-9720472-0-4
    1. Rich Hill (Ariz.)—Gold discoveries. 2.Gold mines and mining—Arizona—
    Rich Hill (Mining District)—History. I. Title.
F817.Y3 C76 2002

Copyright © 2002 by Golden Retriever Publications

All rights reserved. No part of this publication may be reproduced, stored in a
retrieval system, or transmitted, in any form or by any means, electronic, mechanical, photocopying, recording, or otherwise, without the prior written permission of
the publisher. Printed in the United States of America

First printing, May 2002

Dedications

To all the great ladies of the West
  —MKC

To gold fever, what a wonderful ailment!
  —CTG

To all those who toiled on the slopes of Rich Hill and left no record behind
  —DSL

To Becky; for her love, support, and patience
  —EBM

Contents

Acknowledgments ix

Introduction 1

Chapter 1 3
There's More Than One Way to Find Gold in Arizona
(a work of short fiction)

Chapter 2 13
The Geologic History of Rich Hill
(1800 million to 10,000 years ago)

Chapter 3 25
The Spanish in Arizona
(1540–1598)

Chapter 4 32
The Discovery and Development of Rich Hill
(1863–1886)

Chapter 5 60
The District Matures
(1880–1928)

Chapter 6 70
The Hard Rock Mines of Rich Hill

Chapter 7 102
The Great Depression, World War II, and the End of an Era
(1928–1970)

Chapter 8 110
Rich Hill Pioneers
Interviews with Clyde Thomason and Fred Lyman

Chapter 9 125
Full Circle: Gold, Guns, and God in the 1970s

Chapter 10 137
Metal Detector History, Evolution, and Contribution to the
Rich Hill Rushes (1978–Modern Day)

Chapter 11 153
Rich Hill Today

Appendix A 163
Drywashers and Drywashing Techniques

Appendix B 166
Metal Detecting

Appendix C 188
Desert Survival and Hazard Recognition

Appendix D 195
Claims, Land Use, and Legal Status

Appendix E 198
Additional Hard Rock Mines of Rich Hill

Appendix F 210
Gold-prospecting Clubs

References and Suggested Readings 215

Index..224

Author Biographies 238

Acknowledgments

The production of this book was only possible through the assistance of many individuals. We especially thank Clyde Thomason, Fred Lyman, and the many others that took the time to speak with us about the "old days." We are grateful to Steve Gholson for his support, enthusiasm, and advice throughout the course of this project. Nyal Niemuth at the Department of Mines and Mineral Resources of the State of Arizona provided access to thousands of pages of historical documents, photographs, and maps of the Weaver district, as well as his personal insights and advice. Lorri Carlson provided invaluable assistance in sorting through a large amount of historical photographs and documents in the archives of the Sharlot Hall Museum. Ed DeWitt of the U.S. Geological Survey spent time discussing local geology and provided records of mine production. We thank Paul and Paula Magno for their encouragement, the use of their field vehicle, and for providing a rest stop for weary travellers returning from "The Hill." We thank J. A. Lauretta and Cascade Coast Arts (www.ccarts.com) for providing the artwork used in chapter 1. We also express thanks to Nancy Hall at Phoenix Newspapers, Inc. for her help in researching historical photographs. The resources from the Department of Archives and Manuscripts at Arizona State University were invaluable to us in researching this book. We appreciate the permissions to reproduce the historical photographs from the *Engineering and Mining Journal*. We are also grateful to Perry Massie and the other members of the Lost Dutchman's Mining Association for their support and hospitality. We thank the members of the Weaver Mining District in Congress, Arizona for sharing their thoughts and knowledge of the Rich Hill area. We are grateful to Ronald W. Driscoll for contributing personal information, photos, and the 24K Club brochure. Finally, we thank Marsha Havens for the excellent job she did editing the final version of this manuscript.

Introduction

It is hard to imagine that the isolated region located some fourteen miles north of Wickenburg, Arizona, was once the scene of intense mining activity. Gold was discovered here in 1863 at the base of a granite hill. In fact, so much gold was found that the hill was later named Rich Hill. Stories about large gold nuggets the size of potatoes acted like an irresistible magnet, drawing in men of all races from across the globe. Thousands of American and immigrant miners flocked to its rocky slopes in hopes of striking it big. Like many mining camps, it is an area rich in history, romance, deception, and of course human struggle.

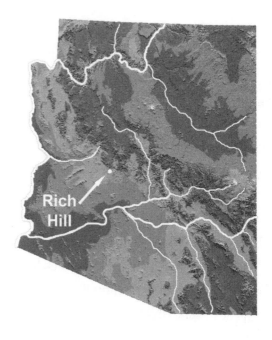

Gold is most likely one of the first metals to be used by humans, though copper may also share that distinction. Both occur naturally as a shiny native metal. On average, gold represents only about one to two atoms of every billion in the Earth's crust. All the gold ever mined since the dawn of civilization probably totals less than 115,000 tons (over 4.7 billion ounces). With a specific gravity of 19.3 grams/cm^3, gold is one of the densest naturally occurring minerals. For reference, lead has a specific gravity of 11.3 g/cm^3 while water is about 1 g/cm^3. Because of its high density, you could fit all the gold ever mined within a cube slightly larger than 60 feet by 60 feet by 60 feet! Gold is non-ferrous and therefore will not be attracted to a magnet. Gold melts at about 1063°C (1971°F), though gold specimens and nuggets will melt at lower temperatures due to their naturally alloyed silver content. Because of its high electrical conductivity and chemical inertness, more than half of the world's gold production is used for industrial applications such as electronics, microchips, aerospace use, satellites, specialty alloys, and dentistry.

The alluvial gold of Rich Hill and the Weaver District is generally of high purity and ranges from dust to documented nuggets of over several troy pounds (see the nugget table, p. 141). The average size of gold from the alluvial deposits of Weaver Creek is described as "the size of flaxseed." Nuggets as large as "Irish potatoes" were found on the top of Rich Hill, giving the famous Potato Patch its name. This patch is reported to have produced up to 2000 ounces from a single acre of ground. Abraham Peeples was rumored to have collected over 300 ounces of loose nuggets in a single day. As recently as the 1930s, nuggets weighing in excess of 20 ounces were still being found. In the spring of 2000, a husband and wife team found a 25-ounce nugget with a metal detector, and in early 2002 a 10-ounce nugget was found. Total production of alluvial gold from the Weaver District is estimated to be over 100,000 ounces (about 4 tons!), but the true total is likely much higher, as most early miners and later "high graders" did not report their finds.

The primary purpose of this book is to understand the history of the area surrounding Rich Hill, Arizona, particularly as it relates to the origin, distribution, and recovery of gold. This history is recorded in many different forms such as the geologic record, travel logs of Spanish explorers, regional legends, historical archives, mining records, interviews with lifetime residents of the area, newspaper stories, and our own personal experiences. In this volume we present a summary of all these records as we best understand them.

Chapter 1

There's More Than One Way to Find Gold in Arizona

(a work of short fiction)

Francisco Vega stood at the top of Rich Hill and surveyed the town of Weaver below him. The town's stone buildings and wood shacks were distributed randomly among the rough, rounded granite boulders that dominated the landscape. An occasional barking dog or bleating goat was the only sign of life in town. A recent rainstorm had provided some water, and a small trickle wound its way around the scraggly desert vegetation that grew in the center of Weaver Creek. For the residents of Weaver, the rain was a godsend and most of the population were out in the desert sluicing the red soils, hoping to find enough gold for a good dinner or bottle of hooch. Seven years ago a bunch of lucky bastards had struck it rich in this very spot. The word had quickly spread through the Southwest. "There're nuggets as big as potatoes," they cried, "more than a man can pick up in a month!" This had brought damn near every prospector west of the Mississippi to the area. They had built this scrap hole known as Weaver almost overnight. The bonanza didn't last long and most of the prospectors had moved on to greener pastures.

Vega rode into town earlier that year and quickly took a shine to the place. He gathered together every murderer, robber, cattle rustler, and thief within a hundred miles. With this band of ruffians he took over the town of Weaver. Now he was planning to get his first gold. Only he wasn't digging it out of the ground. He knew an easier way to get it than that.

"Hey Sanchez," he elbowed the man next to him, "get the boys together tonight, we got some business to take care of."

Later that evening Vega closely surveyed the motley crew that surrounded the campfire. "Who would be the best man for the job?" he wondered. "I need somebody that's quick and stealthy and not afraid to take what he wants."

"All right boys," Vega boomed to the crowd, "here's the deal. I got word from Stanton over at Antelope Station that a shipment of gold is coming down the Wickenburg road day after tomorrow…and I want it. This is supposed to be the big one, boys, all the gold that Johnson has been mining for the past six months. Stanton says he's shipping it to the San Francisco mint, only I have a feeling that it won't quite make it there." He ended that last statement with a mighty bear of a laugh. Most of the other men joined in either out of shared greed or fear of upsetting their boss, something that nobody wanted to see.

"I need three men to hit that stage, now who's up for it?" As he finished that question he scanned the eyes of the men, trying to peer into their souls and see who was up for the job. His eyes fixed on one man whose pupils were an opening into the darkest pit Vega had ever stared down. "Sanchez, you're in charge," he belted out. "Who wants to join him, and remember the men that bring back the gold get double their share of the loot. If that doesn't get you interested then maybe you should go run the tea house in Prescott." He ended this statement with another of his grizzly bear laughs that went on a little too long and hinted at the madness that lay beneath it.

"Count me in boss," said a desperado named Manuel. "I could use some target practice, and an extra bottle of whiskey this week would sure help beat this heat." Vega looked him up and down then glanced quickly over at Sanchez. Sanchez responded with an almost imperceptible nod of his head.

"OK, Manuel, you're in. Now who is gonna take the coveted last spot?" He made one last sweep of the men in his gang, and then pointed his long, grimy finger at the small guy in the back who was desperately trying to avoid his gaze.

"You, new guy, what's your name?" Vega asked with more than a little suspicion in his voice.

"You, you, you mean me," the meek little man stammered. "My name is Smith, John Smith," he answered while trying to make himself look even smaller than he was.

"Of course it is," roared Vega. "OK, Mr. Smith, you're number three for this happy hunting party. Now I want the three of you out of here at first light. Head over to Antelope Station first thing and talk to Stanton, tell him I sent you. Get the lowdown on this stagecoach, then hit the road for Wickenburg, scope out the trail, and find a good spot to ambush the wagon. And remember, you get that gold at all costs. Don't come back here empty handed or I'll slit you open from your belly to your throat. You either get that gold or die trying. Now let's call it a night, gentlemen, these three have a busy day tomorrow and the rest of us have to figure out how we are going to spend all that cash."

4

Sanchez, Manuel, and Smith left Weaver at first light, headed for Antelope Station. They arrived just as Charles Stanton was sitting down to breakfast.

"Stanton," Sanchez demanded, "where is Charles Stanton?"

"I'm Stanton," replied a man seated on the balcony of the Antelope Station Hotel. "Who wants to know?"

"Vega sent me," Sanchez replied. "He said it was time to repay the favor he did for you a while back."

Upon hearing this Stanton's eyes immediately darted around the area. "Don't mention that in public," Stanton commanded. "People around here think that I am a fine, upstanding citizen and neither myself nor Vega want them to think otherwise. Now let's step into my 'office' and discuss tomorrow's 'business venture'."

Stanton led the three men into a nearby house, closed and locked the door, and pulled the blinds shut.

"Now what does Vega want?" Stanton demanded with almost as much authority as Vega commanded.

"Says that Johnson is shipping some gold to Wickenburg tomorrow, real hush-hush. Says that you know how much and when it'll be passing through here. Plan is to hit the stagecoach between here and Wickenburg, get that gold back to Rich Hill where it came from." Sanchez gave the men knowing looks as he finished this sentence.

Manuel responded with a slight nod.

Smith tried to squeeze himself into the corner of Stanton's house and disappear.

"That's right, I heard the coach is leaving Prescott tomorrow morning at first light. Word is they got more than a hundred pounds of processed ore loaded up and ready to ship to the mint in San Francisco. They will be armed, one shooter riding up front next to the driver, and another in back with the gold. They got a team of six horses, supposed to ride faster than lightning…gonna blaze out of here all the way to Wickenburg. You boys think you can handle something like that?"

"Don't worry about us, Stanton, we can handle those stagecoach-driving pretty boys. Thanks for the heads up, I'll let Vega know how helpful you were. Maybe he'll send something nice to repay the kindness," Sanchez finished this sentence with a slight, almost mocking chuckle.

"He damn well better," replied Stanton. "I got a reputation to protect around here, and it doesn't include closed door meetings with Vega's hoods. Now get out of here and make sure none of the townsfolk see you leaving."

The three men shuffled out the back door, hopped on their horses, and rode west out of Antelope Station, the morning sun still hanging low on the horizon. After riding about ten miles they turned south and started straight toward Wickenburg.

"Keep your eyes open for a good spot to ambush the wagon," Sanchez yelled to the other two men. "Look for a good hill above the road or maybe some thickets just around a bend. Remember these guys are going to be riding like Hell's Angels are chasing them. We need to see them coming and get a clean shot at the lead horse."

"That ridge up ahead looks promising," replied Manuel, "nice and high above the road, right past that curve. That should slow them down enough for us to get a good shot. What do YOU think, Smith?" Manuel said the man's name as if he was spitting it out. "How does that ridge look to you?"

"It looks fine," replied Smith warily. "S…s…sounds like an excellent plan," he managed to stammer out.

"What's your deal, Smith?" demanded Manuel. "We got no room for weak-lings on this job, we need you there backing us up, no hesitation, YOU got that?" Manuel glared at Smith as he asked this question. "If I even suspect that you are not one hundred percent into this job, I'll kill you myself."

"Yes sir," responded Smith as he stared at his boots, "you don't need to worry about me, I work b…b…b…best under p…p…p…pressure."

"Well, you damn well b…b…better," said Sanchez mockingly. "You work right on this job, and Vega will promote you for sure. Now let's go scope out that ridge."

The three men spent most of the afternoon investigating the ridge. They looked at the road from different angles and finally decided to stake out the eastern side.

Sanchez gathered the men together and laid out their plan of attack. "They won't be able to see us here because the morning sun will be at our backs. There is also an easy path down to the road so we can get on 'em as soon as the first horses are down. Now here's the plan, as soon as the wagon is in sight I am going to shoot the lead horse. They should be ripping through here so fast that the other horses will run right into him. If we're lucky the stage will spill and we can take out the men while they are still trying to figure out what happened. Manuel, you take down the gunman up front, Smith you get the guy in back. No mercy, boys, just keep thinking of all that

6

gold. This isn't the time to find your conscience." As he finished that last sentence he sent another penetrating glare over to Smith.

"You ever killed a man, Smith?" asked Manuel after Sanchez had finished, "'cause the first one is the toughest."

"D...d...d...don't worry abou...abou...about m...m...me," stammered Smith. "Like I s...s...s...said, I work b...b...best under p...p...pressure."

After spitting this out the other two men saw the faintest hint of a smile cross Smith's face, but it could have been the shadows from the setting sun gliding across his mouth.

The next morning the three men were up before the sun. They checked and double-checked their rifles and sidearms. Each man carried enough ammunition to take out a cavalry brigade. They weren't interested in a fair fight.

Just after sunrise, Manuel tugged on Sanchez's sleeve and nodded to the north. A dust cloud was rising up from the road, looking like the mother of all dust devils. The three men exchanged glances and then moved into position. Smith was the farthest up the road, just ahead of the bend.

When the stagecoach came into sight, he gave a quick signal to Manuel, who passed it onto Sanchez. Thirty seconds later the coach entered the curve in the road and slowed enough to allow it to make the turn without spilling. Just as the first horse rounded the corner it appeared to stumble and drop. A few seconds later the driver heard the report from the rifle blast. By then the second bullet was on its way.

Manuel's shot went wide of the gunman up front but Smith's bullet found its mark, passing through the window of the coach and splattering blood all over the interior. The coach went out of control as the lead horse dropped, but the skilled driver was able to get his team under control quickly and pull up without a spill.

Once the dust cleared the driver and the gunman saw three mounted shadows emerge from the side of the road, gun barrels pointed straight at them. The gunman on the stage responded quickly and dropped to the ground on the far side of the coach. The driver wasn't as quick thinking and seconds later his brains covered the top of the wagon.

"Damn it, Manuel, you missed your man!" yelled Sanchez. "Go clean up your mess"

Manuel shot a quick look over to Smith, "You sure you got the guy in back?"

"I saw his blood cover the seat cushions back there, don't worry about him, I

Figure 1-1. Art work. (courtesy of J. A. Lauretta, www.ccarts.com)

did my job," replied Smith strongly. Amazingly, there was no trace of his stutter.

Manuel dismounted, approached the side of the stage and took a quick look inside. Sure enough, Smith had nailed the bastard; he could still see some hair attached to a piece of the man's skull that was clinging to the wall.

Just then a shot rang out from above him and his horse dropped dead. Sanchez and Smith rode for cover on the side of the road and got under the cliff from where the shots originated. Five shots more shots rang out and the rest of the horses on the wagon team dropped to the ground.

"That's your man, Manuel," yelled Sanchez. "He got the high ground and he's taking out our ride back home."

Manuel spun around at these words and found himself face to face with the business end of a revolver. A wide grin grew on the man's face as he thrust the barrel of the gun two inches into Manuel's mouth. The acrid scent of urine filled the air and a large stain spread across the crotch of Manuel's pants.

As the man cocked his pistol in preparation of removing most of Manuel's head, several shots rang out from above him. Before Manuel knew what was happening, the top half of the man's head exploded. He looked past him and saw Smith's horse drop with him on it. Smith had left his cover and risked his life to save him. Manuel dropped to the ground and started sobbing.

"I guess there were two men riding in back," quipped Smith. "I told you I work well under pressure. Now let's take care of that fella up above."

Before he knew what was happening, Manuel was following Smith and Sanchez in a frontal assault up the ridge they had ambushed the wagon from. The gunman on top opened fire as soon as he saw the three men approaching. His first shot caught Smith on the right shoulder. He didn't get a second shot. Smith switched his pistol to his left hand and with one shot put a bullet through the man's heart. The silence that followed was deafening.

Smith turned to face the two stunned men and said, "OK, boys, let's go see what all of our hard work has earned us. Oh, and Manuel, I hope you brought a clean pair of underwear."

Sanchez and Manuel traded dumb stares and followed Smith back down to the wagon. The three men opened the door and grabbed the strongbox. Their faces lit up when they found that together they couldn't budge it.

"Damn thing must weigh two hundred pounds," yelled Sanchez. "That ought to cover the expense of two horses," he added.

"Stand back ladies," said Smith. "I'll get the damn box open and we can start filling our sacks with gold." Smith then pulled out his revolver and with his left hand shot the lock off the strongbox.

The three men crammed into the stage and Smith opened the lid. Staring back at them was the largest single bar of gold they had ever seen. Manuel started whooping and hollering and dancing around the coach. Sanchez walked over and slapped him across the face.

"Stop acting like an idiot," he screamed. "Our work's not done here."

"But look at all that gold man, we're rich, the whole damn gang is rich," replied Manuel, bordering on hysteria.

"We're not rich until we get that bar of gold back to town, and the three of us can barely budge it!" Sanchez screamed with a hint of panic in his voice.

Smith walked over to the two men. His confidence was shining through his wiry frame like a ray of sunlight through clouds. "We got to get this wagon off the road, and get rid of those carcasses. The three of us can push that strongbox out of the stage, but we have to work together."

Figure 1-2. Art work. (courtesy of J. A. Lauretta, www.ccarts.com)

Together the three men managed to slide the strongbox out the far side of the stage. One by one they dragged the bodies of the horses and men into some brush off the road. They scalped the bodies to make it look like an Indian attack. Then they doused the wagon, horses, and bodies in pitch and set the whole lot afire.

After this deed was accomplished, they walked back over to the gold bar.

The physical labor of hiding the evidence of their nasty deed had calmed Sanchez and Manuel down. Sanchez resumed his role as leader of the party.

"Well, boys, we got one horse, three men, and a two hundred pound bar of gold. This is a fine steed but I doubt she can handle the whole lot of us. I'm open to suggestions."

Smith surveyed the area and spotted an arroyo off on the side of the road. "Let's bury the gold in that wash. One man can ride back to Weaver and round up some more of the gang. Since your horse is the only one left alive, Sanchez, I suggest you be the one to go for help. We'll head back toward Antelope Station, being sure to keep off the road to avoid too many questions. Sound good?"

The transformation Smith had undergone in one morning was unbelievable. Sanchez looked both men over, his eyes lingered on the piss stain on Manuel's crotch, "All right, I'll ride on to Weaver and bring back some men and horses and we can get that gold to Vega. You two stay off the road. We'll meet up back in Antelope Station."

With those words Sanchez mounted his horse and headed north along the road back to Weaver.

Manuel and Smith set about digging a hole in the wash off the road. They were careful to note the location before they dropped the gold in and covered it up. Once the gold was in the ground, they took off to the north toward Antelope Station.

Sanchez rode into Weaver around 4 o'clock that afternoon. As he hitched his horse his eyes caught a flash of lightning off to the east. "Looks like a monsoon is rolling in," he thought to himself. "A perfect end to this perfect day."

It didn't take him long to round up five men and two extra horses. The group set off toward Antelope Station. By the time they reached the hotel, the rain was pouring down fast and furious. He could barely make out the figures of Manuel and Smith. Smith had his right shoulder bandaged. Manuel had found a clean pair of pants. The two men leapt off the porch as soon as they saw the gang approaching.

"Let's ride," commanded Sanchez. "I want that gold back in Weaver before the sheriff starts asking questions about that lost stagecoach."

The group was drenched after five minutes on the trail. They wasted no time returning to the bloody crime scene they had left only six hours earlier.

"OK, boys, where did you bury that gold bar?" asked Sanchez with a hint of impatience in his voice.

"Over in that wash bed," replied Manuel as he pointed to a raging river on the west side of the road.

Sanchez panicked when he saw the spot Manuel pointed to. "You mean you buried a two-hundred-pound gold bar at the bottom of that river!" The hysteria from earlier that morning had returned to his voice.

"W…w…well there wasn't any water in there this morning," Manuel replied, the grimness of the situation slowly becoming apparent to him.

"Get in that damn river and find that gold!" Sanchez screamed. "All of you in the river now!"

The men mucked around in the mud for over three hours. The rain poured nonstop the whole time they were digging. The water was nearly blood red from all the mud they had kicked up in their frantic search.

"It's not where we buried it," said Smith calmly "It's washed downstream. All we have to do is wait for the rain to stop and follow the creek bed until we spot the gold."

Sanchez ran his fingers nervously through his hair. He knew what Vega did to men who failed their missions. He either would return to Weaver with that gold bar or he would turn south, not stopping until he was in the Yucatan jungles of Mexico.

The next morning the rain had stopped. The wash bed was now a gentle creek. Large bundles of tree branches had washed downstream in the night and collected at every bend in the river. The men spent the whole day walking up and down the creek bed looking for the bar of gold, to no avail. At the end of the day Sanchez looked the men in the eyes one last time, mounted his horse, and started riding south. The rest of the men stood knee deep in mud with blank expressions on their faces. They never found that gold bar. It is probably lying in that creek bed to this day.

Chapter 2

The Geologic History of Rich Hill

(1800 million to 10,000 years ago)

Introduction

The earliest history of Rich Hill, Arizona, is not recorded in books or legal documents, but in the rocks beneath our feet. In this chapter we give a summary of the geologic events that produced the extraordinary mineral wealth of this region and formed its amazing landscape. Keep in mind, prospectors equipped with knowledge of geology are the most likely to "strike it rich."

Figure 2-1. Photograph of one of the Rich Hill granites. The view is from the south of Rich Hill looking north. The granite can be distinguished by its characteristic weathering pattern, which leaves the rocks rounded.

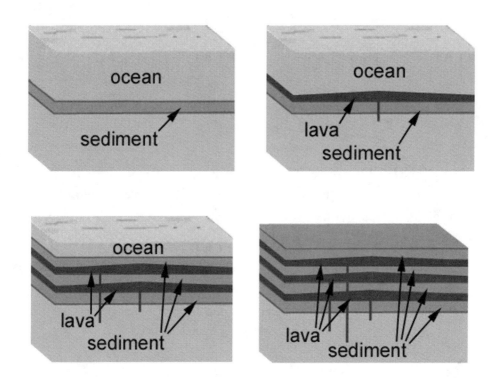

Figure 2-2. A series of cartoons showing the formation of the oldest rocks at Rich Hill. 1800 million years ago, the area lay at the bottom of an ocean. Alternating layers of sediment and lava were deposited on the ocean floor. These layers would later be metamorphosed into the Rich Hill greenstones.

The Oldest Rocks at Rich Hill

About 1800 million years ago what is now central Arizona lay at the bottom of an ocean. Over time, sediments were deposited on the ocean floor. Occasional volcanic eruptions deposited sheets of lava on top of the sediments. The cycle of sedimentation and volcanic eruption was repeated many times. These rocks contained a trace amount of gold, finely dispersed throughout the different layers. As the layers of sediment and lava piled up, those at the bottom were metamorphosed as a result of increasing temperature and pressure associated with deep burial in the earth.

Between 1750 and 1720 million years ago, four large plumes of magma pushed up and intruded through the layers of lava and sediment. A fifth intrusion occurred about 1400 million years ago. The magmas, richer in quartz than the rocks on the sea floor, crystallized slowly deep in the earth and formed a rock called granite. The molten granite moved upward along faults and cracks in the older sea-

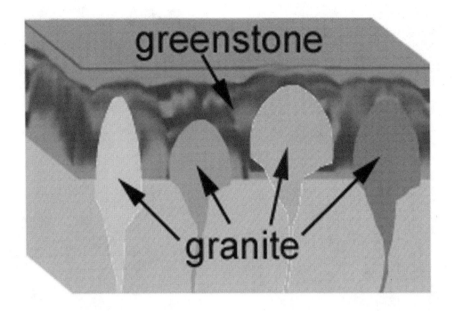

Figure 2-3. A cartoon illustrating the intrusion of four different granites in the Rich Hill area. The hot granite cooked the sea-floor sediments and lavas, metamorphosing them into the Rich Hill greenstones. This event also concentrated the gold that was finely dispersed throught the sea-floor rocks.

floor rocks, and formed bodies that ranged from a few kilometers across, to sheets and dikes a few meters across. When solidified the granites contained 1–4 mm crystals of quartz, feldspar, and mica.

The sudden influx of heat from the cooling granitic masses "cooked" the sea-floor sediments and turned them into metamorphic rocks. These rocks are now called the Yavapai Metamorphics and are distinguished by their dark greenish-black to gray color, and fine-grained mineral character. Due to the greenish color, these rocks are often referred to as "greenstone." Ancient belts of greenstone are associated with many gold districts around the world, such as those in Arizona, Canada, West Australia, and South Africa.

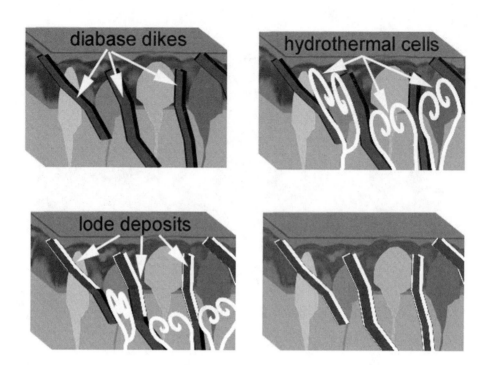

Figure 2-4. A series of cartoons showing the intrusion of the diabase dikes. The hot dikes heated the groundwater in the area, creating hydrothermal cells. The hot water mobilized the gold, silica, and sulfides that were previously concentrated by the intrusion of the granites. As the hydrothermal systems cooled, gold-bearing lode veins were left behind.

Intrusion of the Apache Diabase Dikes

At about 1100 million years ago there was another period of intrusion by very hot magmas, and although a significant volume of rock was not produced, this third major event was special. These intrusions were mafic (very dark rock) and formed elongate dikes that are believed to be similar to other dikes emplaced at this time throughout much of Arizona. These dikes are called the Apache Diabase Dikes. They trend NW-SE and their intrusion created fractures or weakness in the bedrock that had a similar trend. The dikes are up to 7 meters wide, and are sometimes longer than 300 meters. At the surface these dikes have weathered and become masses of chlorite, biotite, and calcite. This alteration has caused many diabase dikes to be mistakenly identified as a granitic-like rock called a diorite.

The diabase dikes do not contain gold themselves. However, these very hot intrusions boiled the deep groundwater around them, which circulated through fractures and porous rock and began to dissolve and mobilize the gold that occurred in low concentrations within the Yavapai Metamorphics. This gold was concentrated by the hot waters, probably as dissolved gold chloride ($AuCl_2$) and thio-complex (AuH_2S_2). The gold-bearing fluids were channeled upward along with dissolved quartz, lead, iron, and sulfur. At the low temperatures and pressures near the surface of the earth, gold, quartz, and metal sulfides were not stable as dissolved minerals. At a depth of perhaps a kilometer, minerals began to precipitate from the fluid and form a solid lining on the walls of the fractures. Over thousands of years, the gold, quartz, and sulfides filled up the fracture zones created by the intrusion of the dikes, a fraction of an inch at a time.

Most of the veins filled the fractured zones in the country rock created by the intrusion of the Apache Dikes. In many cases, the larger fractures fed into a zone adjacent to a diabase dike. Most of the significant hard rock gold deposits at Rich Hill and surrounding areas consist of a gold-bearing quartz vein immediately adjacent to one of these diabase dikes. Notable exceptions include the Yarnell Mine, which has many complex vein networks, and portions of the Octave Mine. However, the veins at Yarnell and Octave have the same trend as the diabase dikes near them.

Today, the quartz in the veins is generally milky white, and in some places there are hollow vugs that contain small quartz crystals. Many of the veins also contain gold, silver, pyrite (iron sulfide), galena (lead sulfide), chalcopyrite (copper-iron sulfide), and rare sphalerite (zinc sulfide). The silver and gold occur as fine disseminations and fracture fillings within the galena, pyrite, and chalcopyrite. Most of the gold and silver occur as 1 to 24 micron particles of an 80% gold, 20% silver alloy within and adjacent to the sulfide minerals. Silver occurs as silver sulfide, which, when weathered, forms silver iodide and silver sulfate minerals. Not all late-stage veins contain gold. Some are barren quartz, dark mafic rock, or fine-grained granite called *aplite*.

"Gold" in the galena lode deposits throughout the district average 40% gold and 60% silver, an alloy called electrum. Pyrite lode deposits usually average 80% gold and 20% silver. The authors' fire-assays of samples confirm this ratio for almost all galena and pyrite ore samples. In the Octave Mine the pure galena assays 100 ounces of gold and silver per ton, the pyrite averages 8 to 25 ounces per ton, and the chalcopyrite just 3 ½ to 7 ounces per ton. While it is documented that the Octave Mine and many smaller mines produced many thousands of ounces of silver, there is no report of any visible native silver occurring within the district. Lead and copper production from the entire district is reported at 747,610 pounds and 326,586 pounds respectively. Electron Microprobe analyses indicate that minor amounts of gold-telluride petzite and bismuth are also present in the district.

Today, the primary veins are weathered to a depth of a couple hundred feet at most, leaving most of the gold as a deep lode beneath the water table. Many of these larger deposits, such as the Octave and Congress have mineralized veins of gold-rich sulfide ore that extend at least several thousand feet below the water table as evidenced by mining and exploration drilling. Careful geological investigation at the Rincon Mine shows that there are several generations of gold-bearing primary veins. The oldest veins are the quartz-galena and quartz-galena-pyrite type. The youngest are

Figure 2-5. A series of cartoons illustrating the effects of uplift during the Laramide Orogeny. The uplift created a drainage pattern that flowed from the southwest to the northeast. The subsequent erosion exposed both the gold-bearing lode veins and the granite that would later form the bedrock of the Potato Patch. Because of the unique weathering pattern of granite, which forms natural riffles (see Figures 2-1 and 2-6), it created a perfect trap for the gold.

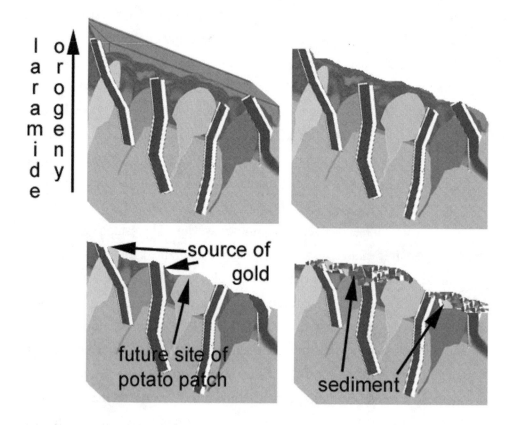

Figure 2-6. Example of natural riffles formed by foliated rock. Stream flow is from top of photo to bottom of photo. Careful detecting of the sediment trapped in the cracks yielded 3 grams of gold in five small pieces. Camera lens cap near center gives scale.

quartz-pyrite ± chalcopyrite veins. All of these veins are gold bearing, but the oldest veins contain the largest amounts of gold and the highest percentage of silver. Some mines contain both vein types, while others contain only one generation of veins.

Laramide Orogeny

Between 36 and 23 million years ago there was considerable geologic activity in central Arizona resulting from subduction of the Pacific Tectonic Plate to the west. This movement caused extensive volcanism, which introduced a considerable amount of magma into the continental crust. All of Arizona was uplifted during this event, called the Laramide Orogeny, and the Rich Hill area was raised into a mountainous terrain. The uplift established regional drainage patterns that flowed to the northeast. Erosion carried clastic sediments northward where they were deposited in local basins.

It was at this time that a lode deposit above and to the southwest of Rich Hill began to erode and enter the watershed. The silver-gold alloy from the vein, with associated sediment, was transported in a northeast direction. Silver is more easily dissolvable in water, and, as a result, the purity of gold increased as it was weathered and transported.

The surface of the now-famous roughly 2000 m by 1000 m Potato Patch was exposed at the surface of the earth. Ground level was not at the top of a hill but was an outcrop on a gently sloping hillside. Running water weathered the exposed granite and produced fractures called *joints*. When the sediment was transported downstream, its minerals were sorted out by density and durability, forming a placer deposit. Wherever the flowing water slowed down, the dense minerals settled out and formed a concentrated deposit. At Rich Hill, the sediment was trapped in the deep cracks in the granite bedrock. The joints formed perfect riffle traps for the coarse gold. Miners have long since excavated these cracks in their search for gold.

Basin and Range Formation

The period of erosion and deposition ended between 14 and 10 million years ago when the crust of southern and western Arizona was extended, causing it to break along steeply dipping faults. This period of faulting, called the Basin and Range Event, produced the elongate mountains and basins that characterize most of central Arizona today. One such fault split the ground at the base of the Weaver Mountains, creating the Hassayampa valley and stranding Rich Hill high above. The cliffs around Rich Hill are remnants of these faults. As a result of this movement, the regional drainage patterns reversed and the Potato Patch was separated from its source of gold. There may still be gold deposits to the southwest of Rich Hill, but they now lie in the Hassayampa River valley, buried under thousands of feet of sediment.

Between 10 and 8 million years ago, the same steep topography that we presently see was established. Rich Hill rose 2000 feet above the adjoining valleys.

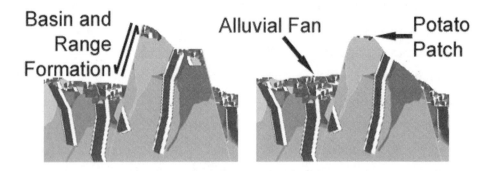

Figure 2-7. Cartoon showing the basin and range tectonic event, which created Rich Hill. The gold-bearing sediment that was trapped in the granite, was further eroded as a result of this uplift. This unique combination of events created one of the richest placer gold deposits ever discovered in the Southwest, the Rich Hill Potato Patch.

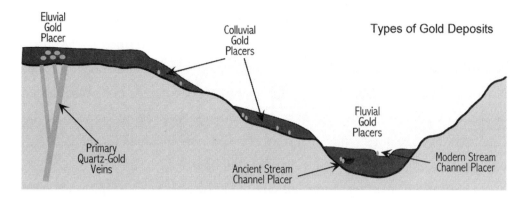

Figure 2-8. Cartoon cross-section showing various types of gold deposits.

Mechanical and chemical weathering processes began to tear the new mountain down. The lighter sand, gravels, and smaller gold particles were washed off the top of the hill. The sediments of the first streams that flowed from Rich Hill thus formed alluvial placers. The dense gold of the Potato Patch weathered in place with minimal transport distance, forming a higher-grade coarse gold deposit called an eluvial deposit. This weathering increased the gold concentration of the nuggets for a second time, making them extremely pure. Nuggets from the Potato Patch average about 91% pure gold.

As Rich Hill eroded further, the type of alluvial gold deposit changed. Most importantly, the local lode veins were exposed and weathered. The pyrite in the quartz veins oxidized (rusted), which liberated the gold from the sulfide minerals, and stained the quartz red. As the pyrite weathered, it produced rusty water that stained and cemented the stream sediments. The abundance of clay suggests that transport distances were minimal and deposition energy was low to moderate. Oxidation also removed some silver from the outer layer of the gold, increasing its purity. Today native gold in the lode veins occurs as thin lenses and vugs up to a few millimeters thick near the surface of the earth. This was a blessing for early miners who were able to mine these shallow oxidized ores and treat them in simple crushers before amalgamating them with mercury to recover the gold.

The oxidized portions of the lode veins were mechanically weathered by water and gravity. The gold was released from the vein and scattered as an eluvial deposit. Further erosion of the hillside delivered the gold to the local streams to form alluvial deposits. These placers commonly formed in riverbed potholes, the inside bend in river and stream channels, downstream from constrictions in rivers or streams, or at the confluence of two rivers or streams. The characteristic signature of the Rich

Hill placers from this time period is the red color that resulted from the rusty staining. These red sediments were shed off the Weaver Mountains and formed a large pile of sediment at the base of Rich Hill, called an *alluvial fan* (see satellite image in color section). They were moderately to well cemented by caliche and clays that formed from the weathering of feldspar in the granite. Thus, coarse gold from the Potato Patch, as well as sediments and gold from the local veins entered the drainages. Today, these Red Placers still contain a significant amount of Rich Hill gold.

Some eluvial deposits from this time are still present at Rich Hill and range in extent from isolated nuggets to "nugget patches" containing many ounces. Because these deposits are of approximately the same age as the Red Placers, they both contain considerable iron oxide staining from the weathering of pyrite, and are easily mistaken for one another. Eluvial deposits are generally less than a few feet deep and are composed of angular clasts in coarse sediment on a bedrock base. If you find larger gold nuggets, gold with quartz, or rough angular gold in reddish sediment, you are probably in an eluvial patch.

Figure 2-9. Photograph of the sediment in the Rich Hill alluvial fan. The Red Placers can often be found as lenses on banks such as these.

Young Placer Formation

Over time faulting subsided and the present topography stabilized. Local lode veins were deeply weathered at the surface and had lost their iron and gold. Most of the pyrite had already rusted away, and the stream sediments were no longer stained red. Erosion, transport, and deposition continued for hundreds of thousands of years. The rivers and streams shifted course, and new deposits covered old ones. The deposits continued to build up the alluvial fan. At lower elevations, the older Red Placers were buried while higher up new stream channels cut through the Red Placers and left them stranded on the side walls. As a result, placer gold deposits at Rich Hill can be found not only in the current stream channels but also as *paleo-placers*, or "old" placers. Remnants of the Red Placers are found as reddish high bench gravels that lie within the upper reaches of Weaver and Antelope Creeks up to 300 feet above the adjoining stream bottoms. As you go farther away from the mountains, the Red Placers are buried at increasing depths by modern stream gravels.

The young placers are still forming today, and are found in the bottoms and sides of modern Weaver and Antelope Creeks, as well as other smaller seasonal streams in an approximately eight- by five-mile area around Rich Hill. The sediments of the modern stream drainages contain little or no iron oxide "red" staining, and though occasionally poorly cemented by *caliche* (soil cement), they are dominantly uncemented. The young placer deposits contain approximately the same distribution of sediment from local bedrock as the Red Placers, with the exception that quartz and coarse gold are less abundant. They are characterized by white to tan sand and low clay content. In addition to about 1% black sands, these younger stream sediments contain both fine-grained gold weathered out of the quartz veins in the bedrock, and smaller gold particles eroded from the older eluvial and Red Placers. Fine gold that was drywashed from Weaver Creek assays between 68% and 85% pure. The distribution of gold is not uniform. The alluvium and sediment just above the bedrock of the channel is usually the location where the most significant amounts of gold are found. Other rich pockets of higher gold concentration, called *pay streaks*, are found where the action of the stream concentrated gold by density separation. These younger placers are reworked each time there is a cloudburst during the wet season. Through these processes, small amounts of gold and sediment continue to flow from Rich Hill and the surrounding mountains.

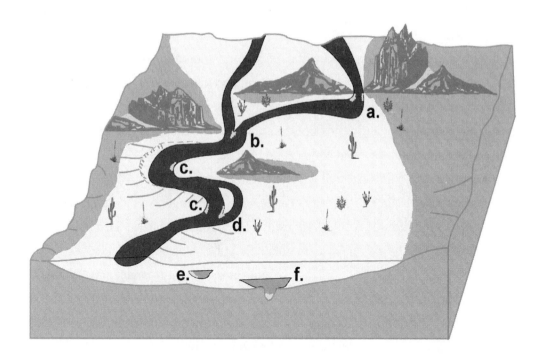

Figure 2-10. Examples of where placers form: (a) downstream from where bedrock pinches a river; (b) in the neck of the "V" where two rivers or streams flow together; (c) the inside bends in rivers or streams; (d) the tail end of sandbars; (e) paleo-placers in old abandoned river channels; and (f) potholes or groves in bedrock of paleo-placers. Bedrock is shown as gray, alluvial deposits as white, and gold placers as light gray dots.

Chapter 3
The Spanish in Arizona
(1540–1598)

The Yavapai Indians

The first humans to enter the area around Rich Hill were the Yavapai Indians. The total population of the Yavapai tribe probably remained around 2000 people. They were a hunter-gatherer society, a lifestyle that required periodic, seasonal shifts in the land that they occupied. They were not interested in gold or other precious metals but rather in the brightly colored copper ores, which they used to color their dyes and paint. Their mining techniques were minimal and crude. The first contact that European explorers had with this group of Native Americans occurred when the Spanish entered central Arizona in the early 1500s. The diaries of these encounters are the earliest written histories available for this part of the world.

Cortés Conquers Mexico (1516–1521)

The Spanish first arrived in North America in 1516 when Diego Velásquez, the Spanish governor of Cuba, sent expeditions into the Yucatan and the Gulf of Mexico to conduct reconnaissance of the surrounding area. Intrigued and excited about indications of a wealthy civilization nearby, Velásquez commissioned Hernán Cortés to explore the Yucatan. Cortés enlisted several indigenous groups to act as interpreters and guides for his expedition. When they arrived on the outskirts of Tenochtitlan (the Aztec capital city), the city's populous believed that Cortés was descended from the white-skinned god Quetzalcoatlin of Aztec prophesy. Montezuma, the Aztec emperor, saw Cortés's arrival as the fulfillment of this prophesy and welcomed the party warmly. The Spanish returned to Tenochtitlan in 1521 with the intent of capturing the city for the Spanish Empire. The Spanish and their allies blockaded the city, denying the populace food and water. An outbreak of smallpox further weakened the city's defenders. The Spanish blockade was strong and Cortés conquered the city and razed all of the buildings. The Spanish government rewarded him with riches, a title of nobility, and fame. After the defeat of the Aztecs, Spanish power spread rapidly throughout the Aztec Empire.

Guzman and the Seven Cities of Gold (1530–1532)

As part of their domination of the region, the Spanish enslaved the native population. The Spanish were eager to learn more about the new continent that they had begun to conquer and relied heavily upon the information provided by the natives. In 1530, Nuño de Guzman, the presiding president of New Spain, owned an Indian boy named Tejo. This boy claimed that his father often journeyed north into the backcountry to trade feathers for gold and silver. Tejo had accompanied his father on several of these expeditions. Tejo reported to Nuño de Guzman that it was a forty days journey north through a barren wilderness to seven large villages that had streets of silver and gold. Nuño de Guzman dubbed these "the Seven Cities of Cibola."

Acting on this information, Guzman organized a party and prepared to travel 200 leagues to reach and conquer these obviously wealthy cities. However, when Guzman reached the northern border of his kingdom, Cortés, who was a great rival of his, returned from Spain. Guzman, concerned by the threat to his power that Cortés represented, proceeded no further.

Coronado Explores Arizona (1540)

Eight years later, Francisco Vazquez de Coronado was appointed governor of New Spain. The legend of the Seven Cities of Cibola that lay to the north had survived. During this period Cabeza de Vaca arrived in Mexico as one of only four survivors of an ill-fated expedition into Florida. The survivors reported hearing of several large and powerful villages north of Mexico. Coronado interpreted these reports as confirming the legends of the Seven Cities of Cibola. He quickly organized a party composed of Esteban, one of the members of de Vaca's party, three friars including Marcos de Niza, and many natives. When Coronado reached Cuiliacan, a city on the northern edge of the kingdom, he sent Esteban and the friars north. Esteban was sent ahead by the friars because he had traveled the land before. Esteban reached Cibola, the village of the ancestors of Zuni Indians in present-day western New Mexico,

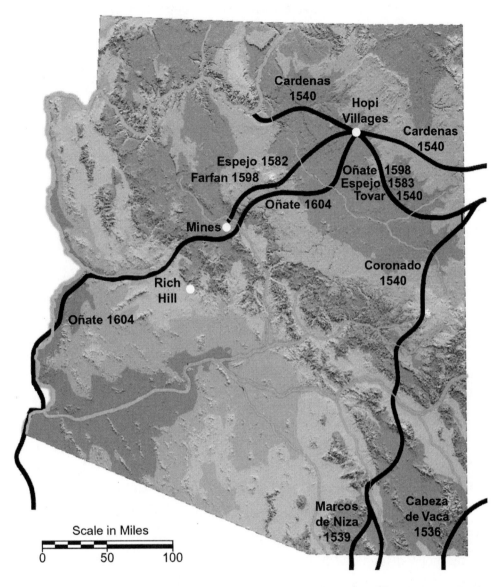

Figure 3-1. Map showing the routes of early Spanish explorers in Arizona. The primary motivation of these men was the search for gold. Only Oñate came close to finding it in Arizona, passing within twenty miles of the Rich Hill deposits.

27

well ahead of the Friars. He was killed on arrival and the rest of his party set free. The surviving Indians met the Friars en route to Cibola and told them of Esteban's death. They fled back to Mexico.

When the friars returned, they reported the death of Esteban to Coronado. Coronado took this information as confirmation of the existence of the riches of "the Seven Cities" told by Tejo to Guzman. Coronado set about secretly organizing a force to journey northward and conquer these cities. The secret preparations spurred rumors that the fabled Seven Cities of Guzman had been discovered.

In 1540 Coronado got a large party together (250 soldiers and 800 Indians) and ventured northward following the route taken by Marcos de Niza. They reached Cibola after a short time. It was a village of about two hundred warriors. There were seven villages in the province, some even larger and stronger than Cibola. The reception was not friendly and the natives attacked the party. In less than an hour the Spaniards captured the village. During the battle Coronado was knocked down and almost killed. When the Spaniards entered the city they found it to be sparsely populated and entirely lacking in the gold, precious stones, and fine cloths that had been hinted at by Friar Marcos de Niza. Because his report had turned out to be entirely false, de Niza was promptly sent back to New Spain.

From Cibola, Coronado sent Don Pedro de Tovar to investigate a nearby province that also had seven villages. Don Pedro took seventeen horsemen, four foot soldiers, and a Franciscan friar. They reached the villages of Tusayan, on the modern-day Hopi mesas, and after a short skirmish the natives surrendered. They presented the Spaniards with some cotton, dressed skins, cornmeal, pine nuts, corn, birds, and a small amount of turquoise. The natives informed the Spaniards of a very large river to the west. Don Pedro returned to Cibola with this information and Coronado dispatched Don Garcia Lopez de Cardenas with twelve men to go see this river. He reached Tusayan and was provided with natives to guide him to the river. After twenty days journey they reached the rim of the Grand Canyon, which they could not descend. On the return journey they found some salt crystals that they collected and brought back to Cibola. Instead of investigating farther west Coronado journeyed eastward, traveling as far as current-day Wichita. He found little gold. Coronado's expedition into New Mexico had proved disappointing and for nearly four decades no further explorations were made in the region.

Antonio de Espejo Finds Mines in Arizona (1579–1582)

Nevertheless, during the decades following Coronado's journey, the frontier of Spanish settlement was pushed rapidly northward and a new line of approach to New Mexico was opened by way of the great central plateau. In the forward-moving column were explorers, missionaries, miners, and cattlemen. By 1580 the frontier of settlement had reached the head of the Conchos River in Chihuahua, Mexico. The military frontier had proceeded even farther in pursuit of marauding Indians and in search of mines. In 1579, an Indian was captured at Santa Barbara who told of large settlements to the north, where people raised cotton and had a plentiful food supply. Upon hearing this, Fray Agustín Rodríguez, a Franciscan brother, organized a party of twenty-eight people, three friars, nine soldiers, and sixteen Indian servants. The party explored a large part of New Mexico and discovered many pueblo villages. The soldiers reported finding silver mines and returned the ore from three of them to be assayed, one of which turned out to be half silver. One friar was killed, as he set out alone to report on the first pueblos that were discovered. The other two stayed at the pueblo of Puaray while the soldiers returned to report the results of the expedition.

The reports of the soldiers greatly interested the current viceroy, and he immediately thought of sending out another expedition, to aid the missionaries if they were still alive, and to explore the territory. While the viceroy was discussing an expedition to New Mexico, the Franciscan Order and private citizens were taking more effective measures. Friar Bernaldino Beltrán volunteered to lead the party. Antonio de Espejo, a wealthy citizen of Mexico, offered to equip and lead some soldiers as an escort, and to pay the expenses of Father Beltrán. Fourteen soldiers, along with several Franciscan friars and their servants, departed on November 10, 1582. Following the route of the Rodriguez party they traveled along the Conchos River to the Rio Grande up to present day El Paso. They continued north for fifteen days until they reached the pueblo region. Upon their arrival they discovered that the two friars had been killed.

Even though the main purpose of the expedition was accomplished, both Espejo and Beltrán decided to explore the area. They traveled west to Cibola, now known as Zuni. There the friars turned back, but Espejo and nine soldiers decided to explore to the north to find a lake of gold said to lie in that direction. He didn't find the lake but came across the Moqui Indians, who presented him with four thousand cotton blankets. He sent these back to Zuni with five soldiers and with the remaining four went west in search of the mines that he had heard about. He found them in western Arizona, near present-day Jerome, and secured rich ores. These mines were said to lie about sixty leagues from Zuni (1 league = 4.83 km). Despite these reports, the exploration of Arizona by the Spaniards would wait another twenty years.

Juan de Oñate Returns to the Arizona Mines (1595–1598)

The contract to conquer and settle New Mexico was awarded in 1595 to Juan de Oñate. The expedition was delayed until 1598, when it left from the Conchos River. The colony consisted of over four hundred men, with about 130 bringing their families. There were eighty-three carts and wagons and a herd of more than seven thousand cattle. After "pacifying" the natives along the way, Oñate established his headquarters at Santa Fe. The Franciscan missionaries were assigned to eight nearby pueblos to convert the natives. The men were given titles to the nearby land that they had explored, thus founding the province of New Mexico.

Once settled in, Oñate decided to explore the surrounding territory. He sent men to the northeast to hunt buffalo on the Great Plains. They brought back a large supply of hides and meat. On this expedition they met the Apache Indians who were living on the plains at that time. At the same time Oñate traveled west to Zuni. From there he sent Captain Marcos Farfán to find the mines discovered by Espejo.

Farfán left Zuni with eight men and two Indians as guides. West of current-day Flagstaff they came across some Indians who knew of the mines that Espejo had discovered and even had some of the ore with them. They offered pulverized ore to Farfán as a token of peace. Farfán begged them to show him the location of that ore and one of the chiefs agreed. As they approached the location of the ore, they came across a small tribe of Yavapai Indians who were "stained" with ores of different colors. As a peace offering the Indians gave Farfán some of the powdered ores. The following is a direct quote from the diary of Farfán as translated by H. E. Bolton:

> And arriving at the slope of said hills, the banks of the said rivers were seen, with deep ravines having the finest of pastures, and extensive plains. As it was late, they camped that night on the slope of these hills, at a spring of water that issued from one of them, very large and carrying much water, almost hot. Here six Indians from different rancherias of those mountains joined him, and next morning they took him up to the said mine, which was at a good height, although one could go up to it on horseback, for these Indians had opened up a road. There they found an old shaft, three estados in depth, from which the Indians extracted the ores for their personal adornment and for the coloring of their blankets, because in this mine there are brown, black, water-colored, blue, and green ores. The blue ore is so blue that it is understood that some of it is enamel. The mine had a very large dump, where there are many and apparently very good ores, which are the ones that have been enumerated.

The vein is very wide and rich and of many outcrops, all containing ores. The vein ran along the hill in plain view and crossed over to another hill which was opposite, where they took from twenty-eight to thirty claims for themselves and for the companions who remained at the camp as a guard to the Señor governor. At one side of the said hill they found another vein of more than two arms length in width, which they named the vein of San Francisco. Here they took fourteen or fifteen claims. On the other side of the other part of the outcrop they found another vein which they named San Gabriel, wide and rich in ores, where they took fourteen or fifteen more claims; and on the other side, on the hill of the outcrop, they found another vein which they named the vein of Guerfanos, wide and rich in ores, where they took ten or twelve more claims.

To mark the location of the mines, Farfán's party noted the location of three rivers. When they asked the Indians about these, the Indians replied that the three rivers and two others that joined them farther on all united and passed through a gorge, which they pointed out to them, and that beyond that gorge the river was extremely wide and copious (probably the Colorado). When asked where the Indians got the shells and pearls that they wore, they replied they came from the salt water that lay thirty days journey away and was estimated to be eighty or ninety leagues from the mines.

Shortly after this expedition, Juan de Oñate followed the route of Farfán and visited the same mines. Oñate continued west and intersected the Bill Williams River, which he followed down to the Colorado River and eventually the Gulf of California. Nowhere in Arizona did the Spaniards report finding gold. However, the route of Oñate passed within twenty miles of Rich Hill.

This was the last of the Spanish expeditions into central Arizona. The land would remain unexplored by people of European descent for more than two hundred years. However, the discovery of rich ores by Espejo and Farfán would live on in memory and legend. Over time the legend of the "Sierra Azul" in central Arizona grew. This legend would eventually inspire the early American explorers of this region in the mid-1800s.

Chapter 4

The Discovery and Development of Rich Hill

(1863–1886)

Pauline Weaver Blazes a Trail into Arizona (1830–1867)

Pauline Weaver was one of the leading American pioneers to explore the southwestern desert frontier. He was considered to be a friend and peacemaker by people from Mexico, the United States, and Native American tribes. Pauline served as a scout for the United States Army, as well as an explorer, rancher, trapper, prospector, and entrepreneur in the American West. He was directly involved in the discovery of two of Arizona's richest gold strikes, including Rich Hill.

The timing and location of Pauline's birth is uncertain. His name is recorded on only three census reports: 1850 Los Angeles, 1860 Tucson, and 1864 Yavapai County, Arizona. He listed his place and date of birth alternately as Louisiana in 1800 or White County, Tennessee, in 1797. Best estimates place his birthday between April 1797 and April 1798. His father was an Anglo-American and his mother may have been a Cherokee. His given name was Powell Weaver and he went by this name for most of his life.

Pauline Weaver first journeyed west in 1830 as part of a trapping expedition organized by Captain John Rogers from Fort Smith, Arkansas, to the Rocky Mountains. Indians attacked the party on several occasions, greatly slowing their progress. By November of 1830, they still had not reached the mountains. To avoid the harsh winter of the Rockies, they decided to head south to New Mexico, which was still part of Mexico. Despite an unfriendly welcome from Mexican authorities the men camped north of Taos. During the winter most of the party deserted and returned to Fort Smith. By March of 1831, there were only fifteen men left, including Pauline Weaver.

Instead of returning to Arkansas, Weaver joined Ewing Young on a trapping expedition bound for California. This was his first journey into Arizona. The party's route was similar to those the Spanish explorers had used two hundred years earlier. The plan was to travel to Los Angeles, starting at the Zuni pueblo, then head southwest to the Salt and Gila rivers and trap beaver.

The land was rich in resources and the men caught many beaver, deer, and wild turkeys. The Apache Indians also inhabited the area and attacked the trappers on several occasions. It is on this trip that Weaver may have carved the inscription "P Weaver 1832" that still can be seen on the wall of the main adobe ruin near current-day Casa Grande, Arizona. The true author of that inscription has been debated for decades. Critics argue that Pauline Weaver probably did not know how to write. However, in 1952, Raymond Duff Weaver, Pauline's grandnephew produced two documents with Pauline's signature. One is on Weaver's petition to the Mexican government for his ranch in San Gorgonio. The other is a legal document for the sale of this ranch in 1853. Pauline also signed a mining location notice in 1864 in Yavapai County with a simple X. The issues of whether or not he could write and if he carved the inscription at Casa Grande are still being debated.

Figure 4-1. The ruins near modern-day Casa Grande. Pauline Weaver's inscription is on one of the walls of this monument.

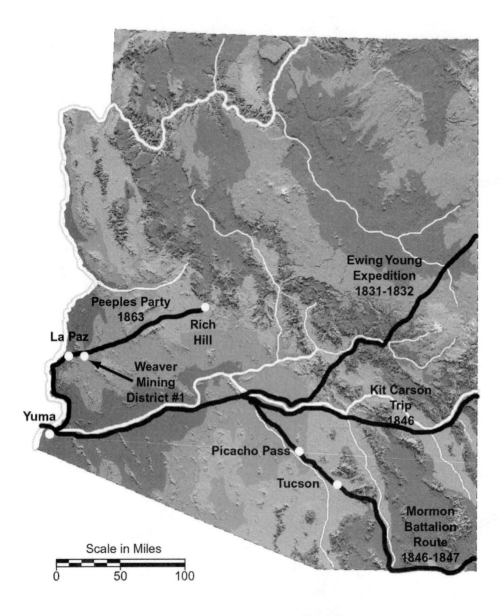

Figure 4-2. Map showing the routes taken by Pauline Weaver on his various expeditions across Arizona. Pauline was one of the first American pioneers to explore the southwestern frontier.

After a hot and dry desert crossing the party reached Los Angeles in March of 1832. They planned on buying and transporting six hundred mules back to Taos where they could be sold at a profit. On the return trip the party traveled on a southern route through the desert regions of eastern Arizona. There was little water on this route and they lost many of their mules. The Young Party, including Weaver, arrived in Santa Fe in July 1832 with the remaining mules and many beaver pelts.

The archives at the Archdiocese of Santa Fe record that "Paulin (pronounced Powelleen in Spanish) de Jesus Guiver (Weaver), twenty-nine years old and a native of Tennessee, the son of Benito Guiver (Ben Weaver) and Cecilia Guamaca (Cecilia Womack?), was baptized at Taos, August 26, 1832." This is the first use of the name Pauline, which apparently was the closest Spanish name to Powell. From this point forward, his name would be recorded in many different forms including "Powleen," "Pawleen," "Pawlino," "Paolin," "Paolino," and "Paul."

Pauline returned to California in the late 1830s or early 1840s where he worked in a lumber mill and then as a rancher. In 1845 he petitioned the Mexican government as a citizen for a ranch in San Gorgonio Pass, California, which he maintained an interest in until 1853. His next opportunity to enter Arizona came in 1846, shortly after the start of the Mexican-American War. He joined a small party led by Kit Carson, charged by the governor of California with carrying news of American victories in California to Senator Thomas Hart Benton and President James K. Polk. They left Los Angeles on September 15, 1846, bound for Washington, D.C., with fifteen men. The party traveled across the California desert to the Colorado River and then followed the Gila River into Apache territory. The party passed through this territory unscathed and even managed to trade with the Apaches for fresh animals. They reached Socorro, New Mexico, on October 6, having traveled over eight hundred miles in twenty-one days.

In New Mexico, the group met Colonel Stephen Watts Kearny, who was marching from Fort Leavenworth, Kansas, to California. Kearny ordered Carson to abandon his mission and lead the troops back to California. Kearny then sent Pauline Weaver to join Colonel Cooke and the Mormon Battalion. The battalion consisted of 397 troops, and over thirty oxen and mule wagons. Instead of facing the rugged terrain along the Gila River, Cooke decided to head south along the Rio Grande and find a westward route from there. Even though Pauline Weaver was unfamiliar with this area, he was appointed lead scout. They departed on October 19, 1846.

After a long journey, made more difficult by Pauline's unfamiliarity with the area, the battalion entered southeastern Arizona. They passed through Tucson and headed north for the Gila River, and back to familiar territory for Pauline. From there the battalion traveled to the Colorado River and then across the California desert. They arrived in San Diego on January 21, 1847, too late to be involved in combat. The

PAULINE WEAVER

Figure 4-3. The only known image of Pauline Weaver. (courtesy of Sharlot Hall Museum)

Mormon Battalion was discharged and Pauline returned to his San Gorgonio ranch east of Los Angeles, which, along with most of California, Arizona, and New Mexico, was now part of the United States.

For the next ten years Pauline continued to make occasional trips into Arizona. In 1857 he left California for good and moved to Fort Yuma, located in southwestern Arizona, to trap beaver and explore the area. While there he accompanied George A. Johnson on one of the first steamboat explorations of the Colorado River.

The next year gold was discovered along the Gila River, about twenty miles from Yuma, leading to the founding of Gila City. By 1861 the population had swelled to over 1200 people. The discovery of gold prompted Pauline to head to Gila City. He didn't find much gold, but he caught the fever and began to prospect all over western Arizona.

Weaver's first find was on the California side of the Colorado River, approximately twenty miles south of La Paz. In 1862 he found more gold on the eastern side of the Colorado River, about 110 miles north of Yuma. His first big bonanza occurred that same year, in an area about seven miles east of La Paz. Weaver and others were trapping along the Colorado River and making occasional expeditions into the surrounding mountains to prospect for gold. In one small gulch, which they named El Arollo de la Tenaja, Weaver found two or three dollars worth of gold. During one of his visits to Fort Yuma, Weaver showed his finds to Don Jose M. Redondo. Redondo followed Weaver back up the Colorado to investigate the area. Supposedly, the first pan of dirt he worked contained a two-ounce nugget as well as several smaller pieces of gold.

News of Redondo's find spurred a gold rush into the area, which was renamed the Weaver Mining District. Over five thousand men entered the area looking for gold. At first the area looked promising and many men struck it rich. However, the placer miners soon ran into a problem common in Arizona: lack of water kept miners from setting up the hydraulic workings needed to recover much of the fine gold. Eight years later, in 1870, the bonanza had ended.

Pauline left the area even earlier, when he was hired as a scout for the Union Army during the Civil War. The Confederate Army had claimed Arizona and New Mexico for the South. The United States sent Colonel James H. Carleton to contest this claim. Carleton decided to capture Tucson, which was being held by the Confederates. He hired Pauline to advise him on the best route to take and to assess possible routes of Confederate retreat. Soon after, word reached the army that a large number of Confederate troops were passing through western New Mexico. Pauline surmised that they would follow the same route that his party took during the 1831 Ewing Young expedition as far as the Gila River and then head south to Tucson. Following this suggestion, Carleton sent a detachment of riders ahead. On April 15, 1862, they encountered the Arizona Volunteers, an independent company of Confederate troops commanded by Captain Sherod Hunter, at Picacho Pass. Lt. Barrett, a Union officer, was the only casualty. The encounter ended by mutual withdrawal. This was the largest Civil War battle in Arizona. On May 20 three Union columns entered Tucson, one week after rebel troops had withdrawn. Carleton entered the city on June 8 and reclaimed Arizona and New Mexico for the Union.

After the Civil War, Pauline returned to the Weaver Mining District and continued his search for gold. The biggest obstacle to prospecting in most of Arizona was the hostility of the Native Americans. On March 15 and 16, 1863, Pauline invited the leaders of most of the tribes in the area to peace negotiations. Together the Indian leaders and Pauline divided central and western Arizona into distinct hunting and gathering sections. Each section was assigned to different tribes and families. However, the treaty had no official U.S. sanction and the flow of miners into the area was so heavy that most didn't bother to learn of the treaty and instead shot any Indian on sight.

Several weeks after this meeting, Pauline met Abraham Harlow Peeples in Yuma. Peeples had been prospecting in the Sierra Nevada Mountains in California to little avail and decided to try his luck in Arizona. Peeples was inspired in part by the legends of the "Sierra Azul" mines discovered by the Spanish explorers three hundred years earlier. The Spanish did not find gold, only silver and copper, but the legend had grown over the years and many miners were convinced that there was an ancient Spanish gold mine to be found. The Sierra Azul was supposedly located somewhere in the Verde River valley, an area that was inhabited by the Tonto Apache and Yavapai Indians, tribes that were not known to welcome Euro-American guests onto their land. Because of this, the area had remained largely unexplored for three centuries.

Acting on information from Henry Wickenburg, the party targeted an area near the Hassayampa River. Wickenburg claimed to have traveled with a small party to a location near current-day Stanton, Arizona, in 1862. There the local Indians pointed out the mountain now known as Rich Hill and told him that gold could be found there.

This was a better location than the Verde valley because the Apache Indians did not inhabit the region. A party of ten men left Yuma on April 1, 1863, that included Pauline Weaver, Henry Wickenburg, and Abraham Peeples to return to the area and look for gold.

The Weaver-Wickenburg-Peeples party journeyed up the Colorado River to La Paz. They then went east across the Plomosa Range and up Cullen valley. Henry Wickenburg did not continue on with the party. Instead, he struck out on his own and discovered the fabulously productive Vulture Mine. The rest of the group arrived at the base of Rich Hill in late May. The area was rich in game and Peeples shot three antelope on a hunting expedition. As a result he named the mountain to the north of Rich Hill Antelope Mountain and a nearby drainage Antelope Creek. As the meat was drying, a few of the men went prospecting in the nearby creek bed (which they named Weaver Creek in honor of their guide) and immediately found gold. Before even making camp many of the men set about working the creek using butcher knives and filling their drinking cups with gold. In a couple of hours they picked up over $1800 in gold (1 oz = $20). The next day, four members of the party went searching for their horses, which had strayed during the night. In the evening, they returned with the horses and a large quantity of gold nuggets that they had found on the hilltop. They reported that the top of the hill was literally graveled with gold nuggets. This was certainly unexpected since placer gold deposits had never been found in such a location. The next morning the party went to the top of the hill and found numerous chunks of native gold as big as potatoes littering the ground of a gently sloping basin, hence the basin's nickname Potato Patch. In about a month, they collected all the gold that was visible at the surface.

Although the easy gold was quickly worked out, the men continued digging the gravels with excellent success. In fact, their supplies ran out before their luck did. Pauline Weaver volunteered to lead some of the men to Maricopa Wells, on the Butterfield stage route, to get flour, sugar, coffee, and other necessary supplies. At villages along the way, he ran into a number of Americans, including Jack Swilling. Swilling and several others joined the men on their return journey and staked out claims for themselves. Word spread quickly about the finds at Rich Hill and another placer gold strike about twenty-five miles north of this area found by Joseph R. Walker.

These discoveries prompted a gold rush into the area, which was officially designated Weaver District No. 2. The Yavapai County official record describes the districts boundaries as:

> Commencing at the mouth or sink of the Hassayampa Creek following up the eastern bank of said creek to the banks of the southern boundary line of Walker's; thence west to the head of the Canyon of the St. Maria, thence southerly to the Indian Springs, continuing in said direction crossing Date Creek near the Indian Cemetery ten miles from said crossing, thence east to place of beginning.

During the height of the gold rush, Pauline was bringing in about twenty-five pounds of gold each week. One man reportedly found a nugget worth nine hundred dollars. The placer miners were panning out about fifty to seventy-five dollars worth of gold each day. The area was worked extensively just following these discoveries. It is estimated that more than 25,000 ounces of gold were found at and around Rich Hill in the first five years. Pauline's son Ben decided to join his father in the Rich Hill gold fields in the summer of 1863. On his first day of prospecting, his party found the first gold-quartz lode in the district.

Almost overnight the area became a scene of intense mining activity and the population quickly reached 1200 to 1500 people. A tent city, named Weaverville, in honor of Pauline Weaver, cropped up at the base of Rich Hill. Gradually, more permanent buildings made of rock and wood were constructed.

As the town grew and its wealth increased so did its reputation for wickedness. The miners invested their time and money in the local saloons, gambling dens, dance halls, and rapidly growing red-light district. Amazingly, their wealth seemed to vanish as quickly as it was found. The town was at the end of the stage line and many outlaws made Weaverville their hideout. The town was so tough that local lawmen were afraid to enter.

More gold was discovered on the other side of Rich Hill, roughly two miles northwest of Weaverville, whose name was shortened to Weaver. This attracted more miners and another town sprung into existence. A stage route was quickly established between Wickenburg and Prescott. The road ran from Weaver, through the new town called Antelope Station, and up the Weaver Mountains to Yarnell. From there it crossed a long, flat valley, where Abraham Peeples established a ranch.

The influx of thousands of miners into the area increased tensions between the Native Americans and the Anglo-American population. In December 1863, two Apache Indians were killed in Weaver. Prior to this, relations between the miners and the native population were friendly. The Indians routinely brought in firewood to trade for flour, sugar, and tobacco. However, these two Indians stayed around town until midnight, then snuck back in and stole some animals. On their next visit to the town, they were questioned about the missing horses. They tried to run but the settlers caught up to them. One of the Apaches grabbed a pistol from a bystander but both men were killed before getting a shot off. As a result, other Indians stopped coming into Weaver to trade. Instead, they started a campaign of cattle and horse rustling that made every unguarded animal a target for theft.

Later that year, eleven Apaches waylaid a group of three Mexicans who were out from Weaver collecting grass to feed their horses, goats, and cows. The Indians demanded the mules, rifles, and clothes and then sent the group back into town buck-naked.

In February 1864, the U.S. Army established Fort Whipple in the area to protect the miners and the mineral resources from Indian attacks. Pauline gave up mining and again took a job as a military scout.

The next month, three miners were attacked and killed by a large band of Tonto Apaches in the Hassayampa River canyon. The war party continued on and attacked a group of Mexican settlers on their way to nearby Walnut Grove, killing five people. For the next ten years, all Indians were considered hostile regardless of tribe. There were several Indian raids on Pauline's ranch and on April 10, 1865, Apaches attacked and killed his son.

In July 1864 an election was held to determine whether Prescott or Weaver would be the territorial capital of Arizona. Weaver was in the Third District and was entitled to three councilmen and four representatives in the territorial government. It is said that Weaver lost the election to Prescott because its residents were too busy drinking and watching dancing girls to go out and vote.

American settlers started to move into the Verde valley and displace the native population, who resisted. In response the army established Fort Lincoln at the confluence of Beaver Creek and the Verde River. Pauline Weaver was assigned to this regiment. The Verde valley was filled with marshes and swamps that were excellent breeding grounds for mosquitoes. Malaria was endemic to this area and Pauline's habit of sleeping near the river led to his contraction of the disease. On June 21, 1867, the soldiers of Fort Lincoln found him dead in his tent.

His obituary, placed in the July 27, 1867, edition of *The Arizona Guardian*, reads:

> Powell Weaver or Pauline Weaver, a noted trapper and pathfinder, and the oldest of the American Settlers is dead. His decease was congestive chills and he expired at Camp Lincoln on the Verde, 50 miles east of Prescott on the 21st of June, where he was buried by the Companions of the 14th regiment, for which he had been acting as a guide in Indian Scouting.
>
> He first to came to Arizona in 1830 more than 30 years before its organization as a Territory, and in 1863 with Walker opened up this central region and the famous Weaver and Walker diggings. He rests after a career of 3 score years and 10, so eventful that the simplest record of its incidents will read like a romance. His body sleeps as he would have it amidst the Grand Mountains which he loved to explore and the rude solitude of which he preferred beyond all the excitement and ease of civilization and society.
>
> Earth lie gently on his aged bones

Figure 4-4.The monument to Pauline Weaver can still be seen in Prescott, Arizona, near the Sharlot Hall Museum.

When the Indian wars ceased in Arizona, many military posts were closed. Camp Lincoln was abandoned in 1890. J. H. Lee was given the contract to remove all of the dead from Camp Lincoln to the national cemetery in San Francisco. Lee was another pioneer of the Old West and had known many of the men buried at Camp Lincoln. Up to the time he died, Lee would often admit that he thought Pauline should be given an honored spot in Prescott.

In 1927, Judge Edmund Wells, a well-respected citizen of Prescott, published an embellished version of Pauline's biography as *Argonaut Tales*. The book was extremely popular and created a renewed interest in the story of Pauline Weaver. Alpheus H. Favour, an attorney and close friend of Judge Wells, spearheaded a petition to the War Department to have Pauline's remains exhumed and moved to Prescott. He also convinced the Arizona Legislature to pay for the construction of a monument. The Boy Scouts of Prescott and the school children of Yavapai County collected pennies, nickels, and dimes to pay the cost of transporting the remains from San Francisco to Prescott. The monument was dedicated on October 27, 1929, and still stands near downtown Prescott.

Life on the Arizona Frontier

A glimpse of the area at this time in history is given in this article from the *San Francisco Bulletin*:

> Letter from Arizona
> (From an Occasional Correspondent)
> —Wickenburg, Yavapai County— Arizona, August 23, 1865
> A Trip Across the Country—Glances at the Mines and Ranches
>
> Having just arrived at this place from Prescott, I cannot employ my time better than in jotting down a few descriptive items relating to matters and things here. I started from Prescott, the capital, on the morning of the 23rd instant, in company with some six or seven candidates for the various offices to be filled at the coming election. The party was composed of men of all shades of politics, and our tedious and somewhat dangerous trip over steep mountains, rugged trails, mesas and river beds, was made pleasant by the good nature and wit for which frontiersmen are proverbial. Our ride from Prescott to the Hassayamp River up Granite Creek was devoid of interest, with the exception of that we took in the magnificent mountain scenery and keeping a vigilant watch for our wary foes—the Apaches. We soon got to Upper Hassayamp River, a very beautiful stream of good water. The mountains bordering on this river present a grand and lofty appearance, and are studded with quartz lodes that will at no distant day be made

Figure 4-5. Photograph of Weaver, Arizona, circa 1900. (courtesy of Sharlot Hall Museum)

to give a good account of themselves. The mountains are covered with pines; the foothills with a thrifty growth of oaks, juniper etc. Grass of a good quality is everywhere to be found. In some places the trail is very rough. About 8 o'clock in the evening we arrived, hungry and tired, at the settlements at Walnut Grove, on the Hassayamp. We unsaddled, attended to the wants of the animals, and then, by invitation of the hospitable owners of the place, partook of an excellent supper of bacon, cabbage, green corn, peas, and various other delicacies to which most of us had for a long time been perfect strangers. There are four ranches at this place, and I here assert that in no country have I seen better or larger crops on the same amount of land. Corn, potatoes, tobacco, and all varieties of vegetables, may here be found. There is also one of the finest and most extensive groves of walnut timber I have ever beheld. The region of country around these ranches cannot be excelled anywhere for the number and richness of its quartz lodes. I was shown specimens of average rock from the Josephine, Big Rebel, Montgomery, and other lodes, that would make a poor miner's eyes watery. A shaft is being sunk on the Josephine lead, from which a red,

Figure 4-6. Josepha Gaulindo, a resident of Weaver, Arizona, circa 1900. She operated a goat ranch in the upper reaches of Weaver Creek; during the time goats outnumbered people in the area. It is rumored that Josepha lived to a ripe old age of 117. (courtesy of Sharlot Hall Museum)

honeycomb rock is taken which is literally spangled with pure gold. Next morning we again mounted and rode down the valleys of the river, past the other ranches, all of which look very beautiful indeed. I saw at two of the ranches an unfailing sign of civilization, comfort and happiness—two white, matronly-looking females. They must be perfect heroines to have braved the hardships with which they have had to contend in following the fortunes

45

of their husbands, over the parched plains and rugged, inhospitable mountains that lay between their former and new homes. But the worst is now over; they have with the exception of society, all the comforts that can be desired, and I earnestly hope they may live long enough to enjoy the fruits of their labor of themselves and husbands. The names of these two pioneer ladies are Mrs. Lambertson and Mrs. Stainbrook.

For about eight miles down the river there are a great many fine valleys—enough to furnish farms for several dozen families, with a sufficiency of timber.

We now leave the river and cut across the country for Weaver, distant some 18 or 20 miles. It is the roughest trail I have ever yet climbed over. There had lately been heavy falls of rain, and we found plenty of water. Shortly after leaving the river we saw a couple of sneaking Apaches gazing at us from the top of a hill a mile or two distant. We did not attempt to pursue them. It would have been useless. We shortly after came to a place on the trail where those red-handed murderers a year ago attacked a pack train and killed 4 or 5 Mexicans. The victims are buried close to the spot where they fell, and their graves are marked by the humble emblem of Christianity, the cross. The savages still continue their hellish work, adding, occasionally, another sorrowful mark for the eye of the traveler, that puts him in mind of the necessity of watching, cat-like, places suitable for these murderous wretches to waylay him, and send him after the many brave spirits who have fallen victims to their vengeful hearts.

We arrived at Weaver a little before dark, worn out with fatigue. There are about two white men in the town, and about sixty Mexicans, who just make a living by working the placers. This place was once the most flourishing mine camp in Arizona, but where there is any water it is now pretty well worked out. There are some very rich lodes in this vicinity. The heat is intolerable, and what with the bleating of goats, howling of dogs, and braying of asses, I slept very little.

After a tolerable good breakfast, we saddled up and started for Wickenburg, distant about 16 miles. After a ride of eight or nine miles we struck the Hassayamp at a point where it debouches out of one of the most longest and perpendicularly walled canyon on this continent. We traveled down the bed of the stream and arrived, about noon, at our destination.

Life on the Arizona frontier was not always easy. The story of Mrs. Stainbrook, the matronly looking woman mentioned in the article above, is one example of how rough life could get. The Stainbrook family prospered for eight years after being visited by the journalist who wrote the above article. They continued to farm and her husband did pretty well working the placers and prospecting for lode gold. Then, in October 1873, Andrew Stainbrook got into an argument with his neighbor, George Thrasher. Apparently, one of Thrasher's horses got into Stainbrook's cornfield and Thrasher refused to pay for the damage. Mrs. Stainbrook was in bed with a day-old baby when she saw her husband grab his gun and storm out of the house in anger. Minutes later she heard four shots come from their barn. She knew her husband was

46

injured because he did not come back. Some of the settlers from across the valley also heard the gunshots and came over to the Stainbrook farm to see what had happened. They found Andrew Stainbrook pierced by three pistol bullets and Thrasher dead from a single bullet from Stainbrook's rifle.

Mrs. Stainbrook did not deal with tragedy well. She was unable to maintain the farm and take care of her small children. In 1879 the Yavapai County Board of Supervisors, after being criticized in the local newspaper, authorized a payment of $5 per week for the widow Stainbrook to take care of herself and her children, who had been found destitute and in an "almost naked condition." The support of the county was still not enough for Mrs. Stainbrook to cope with the loss of her husband and the rigors of running a frontier farm. In July of 1880 a report was made to the Yavapai County Grand Jury regarding Mrs. Stainbrook. The report states that her place of habitation was destitute of the usual necessities of life such as food, clothing, and so forth, and the house was in ruin and all the windows had been broken. The grand jury was also informed that the children had been abused, and there were reports of Mrs. Stainbrook beating them unmercifully with a club and chasing the eldest child around with a pistol in her hand. The report concluded that Mrs. Stainbrook might be insane and should be examined by a board of physicians. As a result of the examination Mrs. Stainbrook lost custody of her children and was placed in a mental hospital. She would live for many years to come, however, and died in 1923 in a retirement home in Prescott.

Rich Hill and the Wild West (1865–1886)

During this time period, the Rich Hill District would go through many changes. After several years of intense activity, the gold that was at or near the surface was mined out. Further exploration was hampered by the lack of water, crude mining techniques (reports suggest that five years after the initial discoveries many of the miners were still using butcher knives to dig out the gold), and the necessity of using explosives (which were expensive and in short supply) to move the large boulders that dominate the region. As gold recovery became more difficult, the area started to attract men more interested in stealing gold then digging it out of the ground. The town of Weaver was taken over by Francisco Vega, who was rumored to head a gang of Mexican outlaws. Vega's appearance often startled people. He was said to be missing

Figure 4-7. Residents of Octave, Arizona, circa 1900. Note the tent with a porch made of brush in the background. (courtesy of Sharlot Hall Museum)

both his eyebrows and eyelashes. Weaver was considered one of the best places in the Arizona Territory to hide from both American and Mexican lawmen. From this key location, Vega and his gang engaged in theft, stagecoach robbery, murder, cattle rustling, and a host of other illegal activities, the full extent of which may never be known. Respectable businessmen and travelers quickly learned to avoid Weaver at all costs. Instead, the nearby town of Antelope Station, which was seen as a much more civilized place, began to attract their business.

At the heart of Antelope Station was the stagecoach station operated by George "Yaqui" Wilson. Yaqui got his name by helping the Yaqui Indians in their revolution against the Mexican government, which had placed a $10,000 bounty on his head. He was known as a good cook and for brewing the best whiskey on the Arizona-California stage route. He also raised his own cattle and pigs, and served excellent, low-cost meals. He quickly gained a reputation as an upstanding citizen and his station and accompanying store did a brisk business.

The route from Wickenburg to Prescott was growing in popularity and the stage company decided to build a barn to house fresh animals. William Partridge, an old Englishman, offered some of his land, which was about one-half mile from Wilson's station, as a building site for the stage company's barn and employee living quarters. Partridge, aware of the large profits Wilson was bringing in, opened up his own store next to the barn. Initially, competition between the two stores was lively but friendly. That is, until Charles P. Stanton decided that he should be the one reaping the profits from the stagecoach travelers passing through Antelope Station.

Charles Stanton was born the illegitimate son of an Irish lord. After attending Trinity College in Dublin, he entered Monmouth Monastery in England to study for the priesthood. He was expelled after being caught stealing the silver coffers. A bounty of £1000 was placed on his head in England. He fled to the United States and, on November 1, 1864, declared his intention to become a citizen in the Court of Common Pleas for the City & County of New York as a political refugee. His record of naturalization was issued on August 26, 1872, by the Circuit Court of the United States for the District of California.

Stanton drifted from mining camp to mining camp, trying his luck in Nevada and Wyoming. One of his mines in Wyoming was used as a staging ground for the infamous Slack and Arnold diamond mine hoax. The swindlers drilled holes in the mine wallrock then filled them with uncut South African diamonds. Potential investors would be shown the gems in San Francisco and then be given a tour of the mine in Wyoming. The scheme was about to earn Stanton $20 million when geologist Clarence King visited the site and immediately spotted evidence of the drilling. He knew the diamonds had been planted and later proved that the stones were identical to those being mined in South Africa.

Stanton fled to central Arizona before his investors could catch up to him. In 1871 the Vulture Mine started suffering from a slowdown in production and became the property of Sexton White. He hired Charles Stanton, who was hailed in the newspapers as an expert gemologist and assayer. Dr. John Pierson was hired as doctor. Pierson built a house and office near the miners' camp. Suddenly, many of the miners mysteriously became ill and died. Since they were paid in gold bullion, which was stockpiled and stored for them in the company safe, their savings reverted to the company upon their death. Pierson buried many of them on the slope behind his office. As a result of the loss of the miners, the unprocessed ore piled up. Sexton White slipped out of town quietly one night in June with his son and the gold bullion. Pierson moved up to Peeples Valley, where he continued to poison people who crossed him. Charles Stanton was just beginning his string of dirty deeds in Arizona.

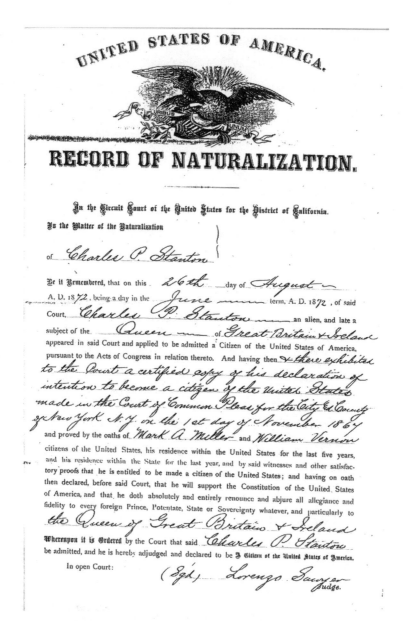

Figure 4-8. Copy of Charles Stanton's Record of Naturalization. Stanton became a U.S. citizen by declaring himself a poltical refugee. (courtesy of Sharlot Hall Museum)

While working at the Vulture Mine, Stanton met a man named Dennis May, who had discovered the Congress gold mine north of Wickenburg. May also had a gold claim named "Leviathan" near Rich Hill. Stanton convinced May that it was not necessary to complete his yearly assessment on the Leviathan claim. He then used this information to blackmail May into giving him half-interest in the prospect. May was disgusted at the thought of being Stanton's partner and sold his remaining shares for $10,000 to Sexton White at the Vulture Mine.

When the mill at the Vulture Mine shut down, Stanton moved to Antelope Station. A few of the residents found it curious that a well-educated, former priest would take up residence in such a place. In 1872, Stanton's diamond swindle was exposed in the California newspapers. While this diminished his reputation as a gemstone expert, many of the rough westerners in Antelope Station thought it was a great joke to play on the bankers in San Francisco. Despite the scandal, Stanton was still regarded as a well-educated, religious man. Like many travelers of the time, Stanton would stop by the ranch in Peeples Valley when journeying to Prescott. Peeples had left the region and opened a store in Wickenburg. Charles and Ida Genung now owned the ranch. Ida didn't trust Stanton but she thought her children would benefit from Stanton's education. His grammar and pronunciation were much more refined than most of the pioneers the children encountered. On one such visit, Stanton was talking to the Genung's three daughters, when suddenly they attacked him, scratching his face. When Ida came running in to see what was the matter, the girls replied that Stanton had fondled them inappropriately. Stanton denied the accusations but Ida trusted her daughters. She grabbed her .45 pistol and escorted Stanton to the door, asking him never to return.

Stanton was not really interested in working the Leviathan mining claim. Instead, he viewed the booming businesses of Wilson and Partridge as the real gold mines in the region. Stanton conspired to have both men killed so that he could take over the stagecoach stations and all the business they brought in. Soon after he arrived in Antelope Station, six or eight men from Weaver, known associates of Francisco Vega, started paying Stanton lengthy visits.

Wilson's reputation as an expert cook and brewer of whiskey enabled him to capture most of the business generated by the stagecoach line. Most passengers were willing to walk the half-mile from Partridge's barn to Wilson's store. Partridge became jealous of Wilson and animosity started to grow between the two men. Stanton seized upon this opportunity and decided to use the men's rival positions to start a feud between them. He sent some of Vega's men to release Wilson's pigs and lead them to Partridge's store. The pigs ran wild in the fenced area around the store and destroyed much of the merchandise. Wilson was remorseful when he heard about the damage his pigs had caused and consulted Stanton for advice. Stanton advised Wilson to apologize to Partridge, which he agreed to do that very day. Meanwhile, a member of the Vega gang informed Partridge that Wilson had sabotaged his provisions and was on his way to kill him. When Wilson showed up to pay for the damages his pigs had caused, Partridge was so angry that he shot Wilson dead. Frightened, Partridge hid in the tunnels of the Rincon Mine. Stanton visited him there and convinced him to give himself up to the sheriff in Prescott. On his way he stopped at the Genung ranch in Peeples Valley. There he confessed that the ex-priest had tricked both him and Yaqui. Upon his arrival in Prescott, Partridge was arrested and tried for Wilson's murder and sent to the Yuma territorial prison to serve a life sentence.

Stanton's plan did not work out quite the way he expected. Wilson's silent partner, John Timmerman, showed up to run the store at Antelope Station after the murder. Partridge's creditors hired a man named Barney Martin to run their station and keep the profits rolling in. Many citizens of Antelope Station and nearby communities began to suspect that Charles Stanton was behind the murder of Yaqui Wilson. Francisco Vega began making regular visits to Stanton's house, often accompanied by a number of Indians and Mexicans. The friendship between Stanton and Vega aroused the suspicions of the local townsfolk, who often joked that Stanton was offering Vega and his gang absolution for their sins.

Stanton still coveted the lucrative stagecoach business, but he had to remain cautious and maintain his image as a respectable businessman. In public Stanton was polite and gentlemanly. He offered to help Timmerman, who had no business sense and quickly became deep in debt. In March 1875 a post office was established at Antelope Station and Charles Stanton was appointed postmaster. One of his first acts was to rename the town Stanton, Arizona. In short time Stanton was also elected deputy and justice of the peace. Rumors were that many unknown names had appeared on the voting lists along with most occupants of the Weaver graveyard.

Behind the scenes Stanton continued to mastermind the Vega gang's criminal deeds, many of which were targeted at Timmerman and Martin. The Martins were friendly, generous people. Mrs. Martin was known to give Vega fresh-baked bread and pies to take to his children. When asked about her generosity she replied simply, "Mr. Vega's children always look hungry." Despite her goodwill, the Martins' house and barn were both burned to the ground. Stanton was considered by many people to be the prime suspect. Not long after, the stage company's barn burned down. The

Figure 4-9. The only known photograph of Charles Stanton. (courtesy of Sharlot Hall Museum)

stock tender, Clubfoot Murphy, spotted Stanton running away from the fire. Murphy was so outspoken about fingering Stanton that the stage company moved him to a different post for his own safety.

Months later, after the Martins had rebuilt their house, Stanton stopped by for a brief visit. Mrs. Martin invited him to dine with the workmen and passengers, but he declined. While the guests were seated, the dining room began to fill with smoke. Barney Martin checked the kitchen, but there was no fire there. He looked outside and saw half of his house on fire. He also saw Stanton running away from the house. Martin grabbed his shotgun and fired at Stanton, but the firing caps had been removed and the gun failed to fire.

One day, Timmerman told Stanton that he was sending $700 in gold dust to Schrofe and McCrum, wholesale liquor dealers in San Francisco. On his way to Wickenburg, he crossed the path of Juan Reval, a member of the Vega gang. As Reval passed Timmerman on the trail, Reval shot Timmerman in the heart, took his gold, and then drenched his body in oil and set it on fire. Douglas Brown came across the burning corpse and reported the crime to the justice of the peace, Charles Stanton, who reacted with feigned shock and concern. Almost immediately afterward, Charles Stanton, acting as justice of the peace, appointed himself appraiser of the Wilson-Timmerman estate and named himself as sole beneficiary. He took over Timmerman's business the next day. Stanton was, at this point, the richest man in Arizona. He started

Figure 4-10. Signature of Charles Stanton from his affidavit in the trial over his alleged theft of an ore sample from the Johnson Mine. (courtesy of Sharlot Hall Museum)

openly associating with Vega, who camped near Stanton's store with his Mohave wife and four children. Residents of Stanton began to whisper among themselves about a "Vega pact" or "Vega compact," referring to the alliance between Stanton and Vega.

Word also spread to Charles Genung that Timmerman had been murdered en route to Wickenburg. Genung suspected Stanton immediately. That summer, a mysterious fire broke out at the Genung ranch at Maricopa. Frank and Dan Genung, Charles' sons, and a hired man barely made it out in time. A careful search of the ruins revealed two wads of kerosene-soaked cloth, evidence of arson.

Another fire broke out at a small store in Weaver, run by a man named Rodgers. Rodgers had confided to Charles Genung that Stanton coerced him into buying all of his supplies from Stanton's store in Antelope Station. Stanton was charging more than double the prices in nearby Wickenburg. During a trip to Wickenburg, Rodgers came across Vega, passed out drunk with a new rifle across his lap. He would later admit that he believed that the whiskey bottle had saved him from the fate of Timmerman and Wilson. When he returned to his store, it was a smoking ruin.

Later that year Juan Reval was arrested and found guilty in the murder of Timmerman. Charles Genung was able to bribe Reval with whiskey in the jailhouse into admitting that Stanton had planned the murder of Timmerman and that they had split the gold in half. He also admitted that Stanton, Vega, and a bandito leader named Raines robbed the Ehrenburg stage on Cactus Plain and split the loot, one gold bar each. Genung reported this information to Sheriff Murphy, who brought in a detective from Wells Fargo. From him, Genung learned that Dr. Pierson had died in an insane asylum in Fresno.

The Lucero family lived in Weaver during this time. They were known to associate with the Vega gang, but were also friends with the Genung's. Their youngest daughter, Froilano, was one of the prettiest girls in town. Stanton decided to have his way with her, and then later bragged that "she had liked it and came back for more." Her oldest brother, Pedro, in defense of the family honor, took a shot at Stanton, clipping his ear. Stanton was furious and offered a $5000 reward for Pedro, dead or alive. Pedro fled to Mexico. Stanton, still craving revenge, swore out a warrant for his brother Sesto and his father Pedro Lucero, Sr., as accomplices, despite many witness testimonies that they were visiting family in Wickenburg at the time of the shooting. Pedro, Sr., was arrested by two deputies and transported to Prescott. On the way there, one of the men beat Pedro senseless with his gun, and then claimed that he had tried to escape. Charles Genung, having heard about the arrest and beating, paid the $3000 bond money to get Pedro out of jail. He took Pedro back to his ranch in Peeples Valley, where Ida nursed him back to health.

After disposing of Timmerman, Stanton decided to eliminate Barney Martin and his rival business. Martin had grown tired of rebuilding his station and protecting his family from death threats. He decided to move to Phoenix with his wife and two children. He sold his interest in the property to the Walnut Grove Water Storage Company for $5000. On July 21, 1886, he closed his shop. This wasn't good enough for Stanton, who quickly set about making plans to murder the Martin family on the road to Phoenix.

Vega and his gang ambushed the Martin wagon just south of Wickenburg. They forced the wagon off the road into a nearby thicket. When Martin reached for his gun, Elano Hernandez, a member of the Vega gang, stabbed him through the heart. Vega then grabbed Mrs. Martin. Mrs. Martin pleaded with Vega, reminding him of the kindness she had shown to his children. Vega laughed, thanked her, then grabbed her by the hair, pulled her head back, and ordered Hernandez to slit her throat. They quickly killed the two boys and scalped the bodies to give the appearance of an Indian attack. The murderers took the strongbox from the wagon, and then set the bodies and wagon afire. Charles Stanton watched the whole ugly scene from a nearby hilltop. The attack was so vicious that the *Tombstone Epitaph* referred to the area as "bloody Stanton."

The Martins had arranged to stop at the house of their friend, Captain Martin Calderwood, who ran the Agua Fria stage station. When they did not show up, Calderwood contacted Charles Genung. Genung notified the Maricopa County sheriff, who sent deputy Bill Blankenship to investigate.

Figure 4-11. Charles Stanton in front of "his" store. (courtesy of Sharlot Hall Museum)

A local rancher found the charred bodies and burnt wagon. Genung and Blankenship traced the outlaws to the house of a local Mexican woman. From her they learned that the gang had stopped there on their way back from the murders and, under the influence of alcohol, had bragged and laughed about their deeds. She also told Genung that the gang had expected him to be with the Martins and were hoping to kill him as well.

Genung had friends as well as enemies in Weaver. One of his allies, Sesto Lucero, told Genung that an old man named Marcos knew where Hernandez was hiding out. Sheriff Mulvernon in Prescott was unwilling to act on the information, so Genung paid the cost for two deputies from Phoenix to arrest Hernandez and transport him to Phoenix, where he would appear before a grand jury. Stanton became worried that Hernandez would implicate him in the Martin massacre and used his influence as justice of the peace to get Hernandez released before the grand jury could meet.

Genung refused to give up. Two of his friends in Weaver kept a close eye on the movements of the Vega gang. They saw the outlaws hole up in an old tunnel in a canyon about two miles north of Stanton's store. The gang brought two burros laden with supplies, indicating they intended to stay put for a while. Sheriff Mulvernon promised Genung that he would meet him at the tunnel and arrest the Vega gang. He never

Figure 4-12. Portrait of Ida Genung, circa 1920. (courtesy of Sharlot Hall Museum)

Figure 4-13. Photograph of Charles B. Genung inspecting ore samples, circa 1910. (courtesy Sharlot Hall Museum)

showed up. Frustrated at the Sheriff's inaction, Genung approached the tunnel alone. He was too late. The gang had split up and cleared town. It was rumored that Francisco Vega went to Mexico. He was never seen in central Arizona again.

The next day Genung caught up with Sheriff Mulvernon. Genung was furious at Mulvernon's failure to catch the murderers and demanded he arrest an Indian who was a known accomplice of Vega. Wary of a possible tie between Mulvernon and Stanton, Genung brought the Indian to Phoenix and placed him in the custody of Sheriff Broadway. The Indian confessed to Stanton's involvement in the Martin massacre, giving the sheriff enough information to have him arrested.

Genung returned to Rich Hill with a deputy from Phoenix and arrested Stanton. They jailed Stanton in Phoenix, hoping to keep him locked up as long as possible. However, there was no evidence to connect him to the murders, other than the testimony of the Indian and Stanton was quickly released.

Stanton's victory was short lived, however. On November 13, 1886, three of the Lucero brothers stopped at Stanton's store and, posing as weary travelers, asked for directions to Walnut Grove. A man named Kelly, who was Stanton's new bodyguard, met them. One of the men asked for some tobacco. Stanton, who was seated at the counter reading a newspaper, overheard the conversation and invited them in. As soon as they were through the door, the three brothers opened fire. Stanton was hit three times, once in the heart, killing him instantly. Kelly blew out the light and grabbed his rifle. He fired out the window at the fleeing figures, fatally shooting one of them.

Later that evening, two of the Lucero brothers showed up outside the Genung ranch in Maricopa. Apparently, they were returning a rifle they had recently borrowed. After a long conversation, Charles Genung came back inside, opened his best bottle of brandy, and started singing to himself, something his family had never seen him do before. The next day, Genung rode up to Prescott, bought a copy of the *Arizona Miner* and avidly read the front-page news describing Stanton's murder.

Chapter 5
The District Matures
(1880–1928)

The Decline of Placer Mining

Placer gold production has been put as at least 25,000 ounces in the first five years of the Weaver District, and at least 50,000 ounces up to 1883. As the first placer gold rush of the district waned, and the fabulously wealthy placer mines began to be worked out by industrious miners, attention was diverted to the lode deposits of the district. By the late 1800s many of the placer miners had called their claims "Deep Enough," miner's slang for worked out and finished.

In 1899 only about twenty men were working the placer fields fulltime, each producing about 100 ounces of gold each month. Despite the decline in placer mining, the manager of the Octave Mine noted that after a good rain most of the shift workers would skip work to hunt for nuggets. In 1905 it was reported by the U.S. Geological Survey in their annual mineral resources volume that only 800 ounces of placer gold were produced in the district. By 1907 the U.S. Geological Survey reported only 400 ounces of placer gold were recovered. Placer mining remained in a general slump until the Great Depression, though many placer properties changed hands and were worked with moderate success.

The Start of Hard Rock Mining at Rich Hill

About 1880, prospectors and miners who had missed out on the first placer rush began to seriously investigate the local lode deposits. Prospecting for rich deposits of quartz-gold was both simple and difficult at the same time. The normal procedure of lode prospecting involved the panning of alluvial samples from all over a hillside. The location of the richest pans would be noted on a map, or with stakes. Then additional sampling would be performed above the rich areas. By this method, the prospector would trace the golden trail back to the bedrock source, or lode deposit. Unfortunately, at Rich Hill, there was little chance to freely pan the hillsides, as they were under active placer claim, and consulting with the claim owner about the richness of the claim almost always failed to provide both the detail and accuracy required for lode prospecting. In fact many placer claim owners would purposely mislead strangers asking specific questions, either exaggerating gold content in hopes of selling a poor claim, or understating the richness to protect their share of a rich pay streak from high-graders.

Fortunately, visible free gold is often found on and within the deeply weathered quartz pieces scattered around the hillsides. In fact, one of the authors located a fine specimen of this type on her first visit. Prospectors would attempt to trace this quartz-gold float back uphill to the source. When a promising lode deposit of quartz was encountered, it would be staked as a lode claim, and samples would be collected at regular intervals along the vein to be sent to an assay office for analysis of gold content. Even if gold were visible, an assay provided the proof of the exact richness of the deposit. In addition, samples with no visible gold might contain up to two ounces of fine gold per ton. With assay results in hand, the prospector was faced with three choices:

(1) Abandon the lode if it was low grade (less than 1 ounce of gold per ton)

(2) Sell the claim if it was rich ore (1 to 3 ounce of gold per ton)

(3) Keep the claim if it was very rich (over 3 ounce of gold per ton).

Most often at Rich Hill, the lode was abandoned as low grade, as most bedrock deposits that were gold-rich had already been eroded away to form the placers. But in a few cases rich quartz veins were encountered, and hard rock mining commenced. Many of the marginal lode vein deposits were worked at a profit during the hard times of the Great Depression.

The most common course of action was to sell the prospect to an organized mining company, or group of miners. Hard rock mining is a very capital-intensive venture, and prospectors almost always lacked the funding to purchase the mining and milling equipment.

Only a lucky few discovered exceptionally rich lodes. In these cases, the prospectors would mine the rock themselves. The biggest problem was usually not the actual mining of the ore, but the processing. The mining would start with the collection of all loose surface float from the vein. Then, using hand steel and hammer, the miner and perhaps a partner would drill a series of holes into the ore. By placing explosives in the holes, a significant amount of ore could be removed in a relatively short time. However, as the hole became deeper, the process of mining became much more difficult.

The most efficient method of ore milling is to process the ore as close as possible to the mine site. This permits the removal of all the rock that does not contain gold, and lowers transportation costs. A primitive gold mill called an arastra could be cheaply constructed. An arastra is a simple yet effective horse-powered ore mill that dates to the medieval ages. A circular, flat-bottomed depression would be dug and lined with flat stones. A tall center post with a rotating swing arm that extends over the pit would be built. A large heavy rock was placed in the pit, and attached to the swing arm by a heavy chain. A horse would pull the rotating arm behind it in a circle around the pit, and ore would be crushed by the rock being pulled behind it. Mercury would be used to remove gold and silver from the crushed ore. However, the arastra was not very

Figure 5-1. An amalgamation pan. The large steel ball would be placed in the rotating dish with mercury to crush and process separates for gold. The dish would be rotated by a belt drive on the vertical fly wheel, probably driven by a steam engine. Note the feeder bins and stamp mill drive shaft with cams in the background.

efficient and had a low capacity of ore per day. Only desperate miners with exceptionally rich ore could afford to operate one at a profit. Furthermore, only the deeply weathered portions of the vein near the surface would yield much gold by these methods. As solitary and small partnership miners could not afford their own processing equipment and expensive stamp mills, the deeper sulfide ore would need to be shipped out for processing. In the early days of the district, this would require shipping to the nearest railhead by oxcart, then transport by rail car to a mill and refinery in either California or Colorado, though the first shipment from the Dixie-Rincon Mine was sent to New Jersey! As one can imagine, transportation costs would devour the profits from all but the richest mines during the early days of the district.

Prior to the 1870s the options for processing lode ore locally were limited to the construction of crude crushing devices and arastras. Eventually small stamp mills opened up around the nearby Vulture Mine, and in 1895 the first small crusher plant was built in the district, followed in 1900 by a larger mill at the Octave Mine at Rich Hill. This mill, and others that followed, would often purchase loads of this rich "shipping ore" from the small mine operators. But even with local gold ore milling available, it was still difficult for individuals to get rich with the costs of mining and the fees that were paid to the mill monopoly. The best bet for the individual miner was to selectively cobble out and hand-sort the richest ore for processing, and then sell the property to a large company that could mine and process the lower-grade ores.

The Methods of Underground Lode Mining

Mining of gold ore involved the drilling of holes that would then be loaded with explosives to blast out the ore from the solid rock. Prior to about 1875, nearly all drilling of blast holes was performed by hand, and many small mine operators used hand drilling up to the turn of the century. Hand drilling, often called jack drilling, was a slow process of driving a blast hole through the use of a steel drill bit pounded by a hammer. The term "jack drilling" was a reference to the "cousins Jack," or Cornish miners from England. In single jack drilling, a lone miner would use a 4-pound hammer in one hand to strike the drill steel that he held with the other. In double jack drilling, an 8-pound long-handled sledge would be used by one miner to strike the drill steel held by a very trusting second miner. The drill steels were made of round or octagonal solid steel bar, and were produced in sets. Each set would consist of a "starter steel" about a foot long and about an inch wide, and additional drill steels that were progressively

Figure 5-2. Two miners jack-drilling a gold lode deposit underground in the Yarnell gold mine, most likely the Juniper Tunnel, about 1914. Light for the miners was provided by the candle held by the man on the right and by a candle wedged into the rock just to his left. (courtesy of Sharlot Hall Museum)

longer and narrower, up to a 3-foot-long and ¾-inch-wide drill. By using progressively longer drill steel, a hole could be advanced without the trouble that would be associated with attempting to pound a long drill steel in the confined space of a mine. The drill steel sets became progressively narrower so that there would be minimal risk of a steel hanging up (wedging) in a drill hole. Periodically, between blows, the drill steel would be turned slightly, and every twenty minutes or so the worker(s) would stop to trade shorter dull drills for longer sharp ones, and flush the rock dust from the hole with water. This is the type of mining that was employed in the early days of the Johnson and Leviathan mines.

After 1880, steam and compressed air drills began to replace hand drilling. These power drills greatly reduced the required manpower for a mine, and permitted faster development of the workings. One drawback of the early drills was the rock dust that was produced when drilling. This dust would get into the miners' lungs and cause silicosis, a debilitating ailment that greatly reduced lung capacity and often resulted in a slow painful death. Miners who contracted silicosis were considered to be "dusted," and the growing number of cases eventually resulted in the incorporation of water jets in the drill to eliminate almost all dust.

In advancing a tunnel, up to twenty blast holes would be drilled 2 to 3 feet deep in a pattern that converged toward the center of the rock face. Near the end of a shift, when all holes had been drilled (it might take several shifts), all tools would be picked up, and the holes loaded with explosives. By the time of the discovery at Rich Hill, dynamite (often called "Giant Powder") was coming into common use. Sticks of dynamite would be pushed into the blast holes with a wooden pole to prevent sparking. The last stick inserted into the hole would be primed by inserting a blasting cap attached to a fuse or electrical detonator wire. At the end of the shift, after the blast holes were loaded with explosives, the miners would light the fuses and walk away with a slow, careful pace. A careless miner who ran might trip and fall. Being knocked unconscious or slowed by a fall prior to leaving the blast area would not be a pleasant way to end the day's work.

Once at a safe distance, the miner would listen for the sound of the detonations, counting each to ensure that no dynamite failed to detonate. If any "missed rounds" (unexploded dynamite) were suspected, the men of the next shift would be notified to be on the lookout. The time between shifts was scheduled to be sufficient for the dynamite fumes and dust to clear from the mine. After a blast, the incoming shift would sort the broken rock into waste rock and ore, and then load the ore into carts for transportation out of the mine.

A variation on the above pattern of mining common in the Weaver District mines is called stope mining. As the ore veins are commonly an inclined body that dipped into the hillside, the miners could use gravity to assist with mining and ore removal. A tunnel would be driven into the vein from the lowest point on the property, and adjacent to the mill site. This tunnel was called a haulage tunnel, and was used for transporting ore from the mine to the mill. From the haulage tunnel, workers would mine up the sloping ore body, letting the ore slide down behind them on the inclined floor of the stope, and into wooden ore chutes above the haulage tunnel. Mine carts could then be pulled under the wooden ore chutes, and loaded by opening the front of the chute to allow the rock to fall out into the cart. In the Octave Mine, and most other well-designed mines, the haulage tunnel would slope slightly downward toward the portal. This made it easier to pull loaded ore carts out of the mine and allowed water to drain out of the mine, which was considered a fair trade-off for the price of pushing empty ore carts up the slight slope back into the mine.

Processing of Gold Ore from Lode Mines

As large lode mines opened up in the Rich Hill area, the companies began to build treatment works at the mine site to eliminate the prohibitively expensive transportation of ore to distant processing plants. Because of the nature of the gold ore, these gold ore mills were of fairly simple design.

Figure 5-3. Cartoon illustrating the stoping methods commonly used in the lode mines of the Weaver District. The stope would follow the dipping vein, and be inclined at the appropriate angle above the haulage level.

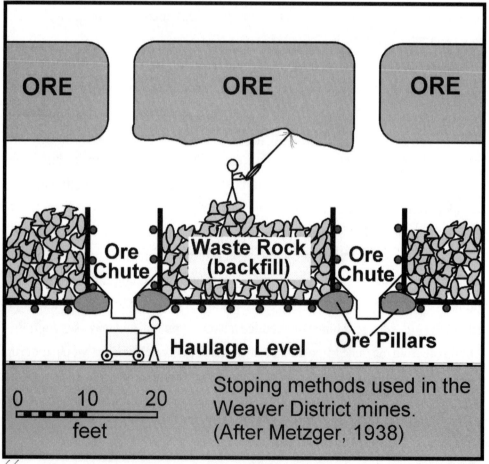

Figure 5-4. Example of wooden ore bins from the Chino Mining District, New Mexico. Rough-crushed ore would be stockpiled in these bins to await further crushing and milling.

The first step in the milling of gold ore was crushing. The simplest and most common method was the California Gravity Stamp Mill, which was loosely based upon earlier Spanish and Cornish designs. A stamp mill bank would normally consist of five individual stamps. Each stamp was composed of a 20-foot-long solid iron lifter rod with a solid massive cylinder of iron, called the shoe, at the bottom. Steam power was most commonly used to spin a large flywheel, which would rotate a series of cams that would raise and drop the lifter rod and shoe of individual stamps in an alternating order. Ore was shoveled under the stamps to be crushed, and when it had been reduced to sand, it would pass through screens on the front of the mill. Between the roar of the steam engine and the dropping shoes, which weighed up to 1000 pounds each, an operating stamp mill was deafening.

The processes used to liberate gold from the crushed ore would vary, depending upon the type of ore being treated. The portion of the lode deposit near the surface was almost always weathered (oxidized), often to a depth of about 100 feet. This natural oxidation process would leach out sulfur and iron, leaving gold behind as a native metal. These oxide ores or free-milling ores were easy to treat, and after crushing the ore would be mixed with water to form a sandy slurry, and passed over a copper plate painted with mercury. Native gold easily alloys with the mercury. Next, some of the remaining gold was collected by passing the ore slurry over a Wilfley Table. The Wilfley Table was a large vibrating inclined table with riffles. Gold and denser minerals would separate out into streaks that could easily be cleaned off the table. With particularly stubborn ore, a final step might be included, where the remaining slurry would be again passed over a copper table painted with mercury. The sand left after the gold extraction, called tailings, was discarded into a pond outside the mill. Mill tailings are often confused by the novice with the mine dump, which is the pile of coarse waste rock (rock with little or no gold) from the mine. Mine dumps are often located around the mouth of a mine, while tailings are located farther from the mine, and are distinctive in their "beach sand" appearance.

At the end of the shift, mill workers would scrape the mercury-gold alloy, called amalgam, off the copper plates. Amalgam would be squeezed in a press to drive off the extra mercury, and then placed into a retort. The retort consisted of a heating chamber into which the amalgam was put and heated. The retorting process is similar to boiling salt water away to produce solid salt. Mercury would boil off and separate from the gold, passing out of the chamber and into a cooling tube where the mercury could be collected for reuse. After all the mercury had been boiled off, all that re-mained in the heating chamber was a sponge-like mass of gold. This sponge gold along with gold collected off the Wilfley Table would be melted into bars. Bars were often cast into the largest size pos-sible, often more than one hundred pounds, to minimize mobility in the event of theft.

Figure 5-5. An example of a stamp mill, circa 1890. The second stamp assembly that was mounted where the author is standing has been removed. Unlike this small two-stamp crusher, most stamp batteries consisted of five stamps.

More difficult to treat than free-milling ores were the gold-bearing sul-fide ores. Below the oxidation zone (usually the water table), lode deposits consisted of gold associated with sul-fide minerals such as pyrite (iron sul-fide) and galena (lead sulfide). Treating sulfide ores with the above method would yield very poor gold recovery. To free the gold from the sulfides, this type of ore was often roasted in a fur-nace to drive off the sulfur. After roast-ing, the ore could be treated in the method described above, but more

commonly would be placed in a large amalgamation drum or vat with a quantity of mercury. Resembling an oversized rock tumbler, the drum would rotate and mix the roasted ore pulps with the mercury to produce amalgam. The gold-mercury amalgam would then be treated in a retort to release the gold.

In 1889 the use of cyanide as a gold-liberating agent in a new milling procedure was started at a mine in New Zealand, and the method soon spread to mines across the world. By 1891, the use of cyanide was in widespread use in the United States. In the cyanide process, ore would be crushed and treated as described above, including roasting if the ore was of the sulfide type. The crushed ore was then treated in large vats by soaking in a very dilute (0.005 molar) sodium cyanide solution while stirring vigorously. The fine gold particles in the crushed ore would dissolve into solution, and this fluid would then be decanted off and passed through a box filled with zinc to precipitate gold metal. A retort process similar to that used with mercury-gold amalgam would then treat the gold precipitate and remaining zinc.

The cyanide process had the advantage of recovering a larger percentage of the gold than the mercury process. It also had the advantage of being a cheaper process, and thus lower-grade ore could be treated at a greater profit. Old mill tailings even contained enough gold missed by the mercury process that they could be reprocessed with cyanide at a significant profit.

Chapter 6
The Hard Rock Mines of Rich Hill

The early lode, or "hard rock," miners of the Weaver District were faced with insufficient capital, staggering transportation costs, primitive milling methods, and low government-controlled gold prices. High fuel costs were also a major issue prior to the early 1900s. Only sparse local ironwood and mesquite were available for fuel, and often these needed to be hauled many miles by pack mule or wagon. By the early 1900s the arrival of the railroad to nearby communities made imported coal a viable alternative to fire the boilers and compressors of the mines and mills. By 1915 diesel and gasoline engines began to dominate, and by the 1930s there were electrical lines reaching many operations.

Even in more recent times, ore and waste rock were sorted by hand at these mines. As a result of human sorting error, one can still find lumps of high-grade galena- or pyrite-rich ore that was discarded as waste on the mine dumps. Inefficient milling plants also spelled doom for many operations with reasonably rich ore. Early operations such as the Johnson Mine used primitive arastras and mercury amalgamation. While this type of operation worked reasonably well with the weathered and oxidized ores near the surface, many hundreds of ounces of gold and silver were still lost in the tailings. The arastra only recovered a small percentage of gold from the deeper and more abundant sulfide ores. Only the Octave Mine used a reasonably effective mill, and even the tailings from it were eventually re-treated at a profit.

What follows are the histories and descriptions of some of the notable mines of the Rich Hill area. Additional mine information can be found in Appendix E.

The Octave Mine

The lode deposit east of Decision Corner that steeply dips into Weaver Hill in Sections 5 and 6 (see map) was long an attractive prospect as a lode claim, and was probably initially discovered in the late 1860s. However, little of the Octave lode gold was free milling, or able to be separated out by simple crushing and panning. The result was that only minor work was done on the deposit until the 1890s, when a syndicate of eight men purchased the property and organized the Octave Gold Mining Company. A small amount of rich "shipping" ore was removed from the lode between

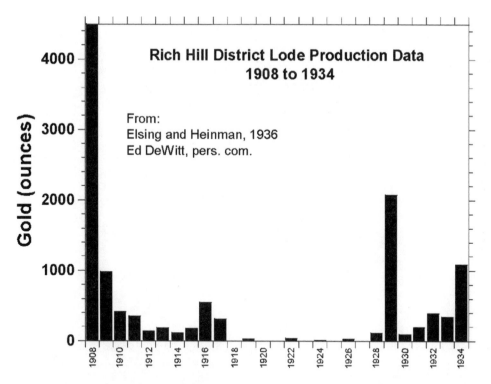

Figure 6-1. Graph showing the total amount of gold produced from Rich Hill lode deposits throughout the history of the district.

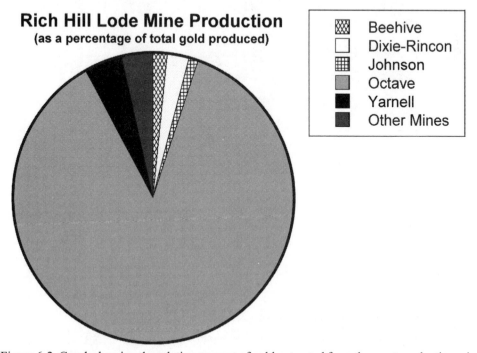

Figure 6-2. Graph showing the relative amount of gold extracted from the most productive mines in the Rich Hill district.

Map #	Name	Other Names for Site	latitude (decimal)	longitude (decimal)	lattitude (min/sec)	longitude (min/sec)	UTM Grid (north)	UTM Grid (east)	township	range	section(s)	Quarter[1]	elevation (feet)
						Mine Location							
1	16 to 1	Schoonover	34.152500	-112.715278	34-09-09N	112-42-55W	3780150	343270	009N	004W	6	W2	3360
2	Beehive	Ziegler, Peterson	34.158333	-112.680833	34-09-30N	112-40-51W	3780793	345055	010N	004W	33	S2	4200
3	Blue Bell	Capitol	34.116944	-112.685278	34-07-01N	112-41-07W	3776430	344745	009N	005W	9	NW	3580
4	Box Placer		34.179722	-112.726944	34-10-47N	112-43-37W	3782026	341764	010N	005W	25	C	3600
5	De Vault Placer	Manurium and Urium	34.204444	-112.708056	34-12-16N	112-42-29W	3785697	343362	010N	004W	18	S2	4100
6	Desert Gold		34.192778	-112.711111	34-11-34N	112-42-40W	3783848	343331	010N	004W	19	C	4170
7	Devil's Nest	Frederickson	34.160833	-112.708611	34-09-39N	112-42-31W	3780152	343270	010N	004W	31	SE	3650
8	Dixie-Rincon	New York, Marcus, Welcome	34.178333	-112.749722	34-10-42N	112-44-59W	3783120	338740	010N	005W	26	W2	4000
9	Dos Caballeros		34.130556	-112.712778	34-07-50N	112-42-46W	3776455	343208	009N	004W	8	S2	3160
10	Endependence	Last Chance	34.156944	-112.723611	34-09-25N	112-43-25W	3780700	341100	010N	004W	8	NW	3600
11	Golden Goose	Barbara Lee, Octave Placer	34.179722	-112.699167	34-10-47N	112-41-57W	3781975	344836	010N	004W	29	W2	4200
12	Golden Gravel	B-J	34.157222	-112.710833	34-09-26N	112-42-39W	3780152	343270	009N	004W	5	NW	3450
13	Gray Fox		34.180000	-112.733889	34-10-48N	112-44-02W	3782052	340227	010N	005W	25	E2	3800
14	Grey Mare	Poncho Via, Skyhigh	34.193056	-112.745278	34-11-35N	112-44-43W	3783900	340259	010N	005W	23	SW	4610
15	Hackberry Lode		34.153333	-112.719722	34-09-12N	112-43-11W	3780178	341733	009N	005W	1	E2	3450
16	Hayden	Empire, Standard	34.176111	-112.709444	34-10-34N	112-42-34W	3782000	343300	010N	004W	30	S2	5075
17	Helen Morris	Nest Egg, Planet Saturn	34.165833	-112.720000	34-09-57N	112-43-12W	3780178	341732	010N	005W	36	E2	3990
18	Jerome		34.169722	-112.718889	34-10-11N	112-43-08W	3782110	341733	010N	005W	36	NE	4200
19	John Sloan		34.160000	-112.722222	34-09-36N	112-43-20W	3780178	341733	010N	005W	36	SE	3675
20	Johnson	Russell	34.180278	-112.701667	34-10-49N	112-42-06W	3783250	343170	010N	004W	29	NE	4300
21	Laurella	Maybe	34.191667	-112.722222	34-11-30N	112-43-20W	3784550	341300	010N	005W	24	SE	3800
22	Leviathan	Maxmillian, Stanton's, Sexton	34.166111	-112.744167	34-09-58N	112-44-39W	3781753	339231	010N	005W	35	SE	3400
23	Lucky Johnnie	Katie	34.174444	-112.724444	34-10-28N	112-43-28W	3782026	341764	010N	005W	25	SE	3700
24	Merrill Placer		34.151389	-112.708611	34-09-05N	112-42-31W	3780152	343269	009N	004W	6	W2	3375
25	Mesa Grande	Mesa Grande Extension	34.143056	-112.698056	34-08-35N	112-41-53W	3779140	343442	009N	004W	8	E2	3600
26	Meyers	Rich Hill Mine	34.155556	-112.711389	34-09-20N	112-42-41W	3780530	342230	009N	004W	6	N2	3580
27	Mizpah	Eagle	34.159722	-112.722500	34-09-35N	112-43-21W	3780177	341732	010N	005W	36	E2	3600
28	Montana King	Phoenixion	34.141944	-112.714722	34-08-31N	112-42-53W	3778303	343239	009N	004W	9	NW	3580
29	Mountainside		34.166667	-112.720000	34-10-00N	112-43-12W	3781790	341450	010N	005W	36	E2	4240
30	Octave	Joker, Bonanza	34.144167	-112.706667	34-08-39N	112-42-24W	3779249	342656	009N	004W	5	SW	3400
31	Pyramid	Stanton Taconite	34.188333	-112.728056	34-11-18N	112-43-41W	3783874	341795	010N	005W	24	SW	3800
32	Rattlesnake Haven		34.151389	-112.726944	34-09-05N	112-43-37W	3780178	341733	009N	005W	1	C	3300
33	Red Metal	Mildred, Lucky Strike	34.180000	-112.734167	34-10-48N	112-44-03W	3782052	340227	010N	005W	25	W2	3800
34	Red Twister		34.178333	-112.734444	34-10-42N	112-44-04W	3782053	340228	010N	005W	25	SW	3700
35	Reese Mine	Fulcher & Fry, Black Dyke	34.197778	-112.740833	34-11-52N	112-44-27W	3783926	338722	010N	005W	23	N2	4600
36	Shaft #3		34.157222	-112.729722	34-09-26N	112-43-47W	3780178	341733	009N	005W	1	NW	3380
37	Shaft #4		34.163056	-112.734444	34-09-47N	112-44-04W	3780204	340196	010N	005W	36	SW	3520
38	Upton Placer		34.151111	-112.726944	34-09-04N	112-43-37W	3780063	340790	010N	005W	36	C	3500
39	War Eagle	Patsy	34.152500	-112.715278	34-09-09N	112-42-55W	3780150	343270	009N	004W	6	W2	3575
40	Wildhorse Placer		34.162500	-112.708333	34-09-45N	112-42-30W	3781297	342527	010N	004W	31	SE	3580
41	Wright	Dogpatch, Rambling Rose	34.185556	-112.721111	34-11-08N	112-43-16W	3783874	341795	010N	005W	25	NE	3800
42	Yarnell		34.205833	-112.747778	34-12-21N	112-44-52W	3786170	338970	010N	005W	14	SW	5110
43	Yellowjacket	Last Chance, Rendevous	34.180833	-112.692778	34-10-51N	112-41-34W	3783306	343995	010N	004W	29	NE	4400

[1] "Quarter" of section listed as SW (southwest), SE (southeast), NE (northeast), NW (northwest), C (center), W2 (west half), E2 (east half), N2 (north half), and S2 (south half).

Table 6-1. Locations of the most important mines in the Rich Hill district.

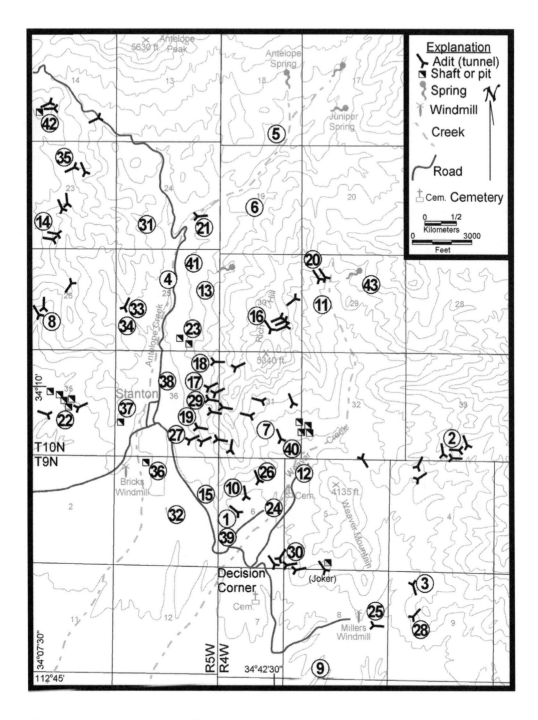

Figure 6-3. Map of mines in the Weaver District.

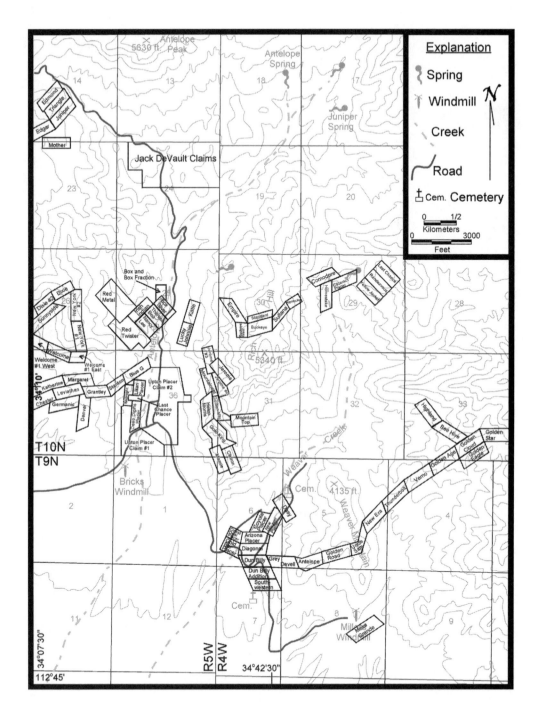

Figure 6-4. Map of the most significant claims in the Rich Hill area.

Claim Name	Type	Date of Issue	Patent Issued To	Township	Location Range	Section
Arizona	Placer	June 17, 1949	William D. Merrill	9N	4W	6
Blue G	Lode	December 17, 1908	Octave Gold Mining Co.	10N	5W	36
Buckeye	Lode	June 3, 1899	Charles H. Hayden	10N	4W	30
Cataract	Placer	February 9, 1901	J. W. Smith	10N	4W	29
Comodore	Lode	October 17, 1898	Hamilton Family and J. W. Smith	10N	4W	29
Coyote	Placer	December 18, 1924	John T. Dowdy	9N	4W	5
Dasy	Lode	December 18, 1924	John T. Dowdy	4N	4W	6
Deep Digins	Placer	March 18, 1901	Annie Peery	10N	5W	36
Edgar	Lode	June 4, 1894	Virginia Gold Mining & Milling Co.	10N	5W	14
Edmond	Lode	June 4, 1894	Virginia Gold Mining & Milling Co.	10N	5W	14
Golden Age	Lode	September 17, 1900	Andrew Peterson	10N	4W	33
Golden Mountain	Lode	February 7, 1897	George Upton	10N	5W	36
Helen Morris	Lode	June 8, 1907	G. E. Lamb	9N	4W	31
Homestake	Lode	January 18, 1899	J. W. Smith	10N	4W	29
Jerome #3	Lode	September 16, 1960	Ellsworth E. Davis	10N	5W	36
Juniper	Lode	June 4, 1894	Virginia Gold Mining & Milling Co.	10N	5W	14
Last Chance	Placer	July 17, 1901	T. E. Peery	10N	5W	36
Leviathan	Lode	March 3, 1888	Charles P. Stanton	10N	5W	35
Lilian	Placer	July 1, 1902	G. E. Lamb	10N	5N	36
Lucky Johnnie	Lode	May 1, 1899	Rich Hill Gold Co.	10N	5W	25
Mamie	Lode	May 21, 1907	M. J. Cosman	9N	5W	1
Midnight	Lode	May 21, 1907	Mountain Side Mining Co.	10N	5W	36
Mother	Lode	August 6, 1896	Frank R. Biedler	10N	5W	23
Mountineer	Lode	June 8, 1907	Mountain Side Mining Co.	10N	4W	31
New Era	Lode	January 8, 1901	Byron Newton	9N	4W	5
Stanton	Lode	December 17, 1908	Octave Gold Mining Co.	10N	5W	36
Sultana	Lode	February 17, 1899	James Hamilton and J. W. Smith	10N	4W	30
Thunderbolt	Lode	January 8, 1901	John Bishop and T. W. Field	9N	4W	4
Triangle	Lode	June 4, 1894	Virginia Gold Mining & Milling Co.	10N	5W	14
Unnamed Deposit	Lode	July 23, 1897	Yavapai Gold Mining Co.	9N	4W	8
Unnamed Deposit	Lode	November 3, 1899	T. H. Field and T. E. Peery	9N	4W	5
Unnamed Deposit	Lode	October 20, 1906	Rincon Mines Co.	10N	5W	26
Unnamed Deposit	Placer	November 28, 1949	George Upton and M. Sanborn	9N	5W	36
Upton #1	Lode					
Upton #2	Placer	November 28, 1949	George Upton and M. Sanborn	9N	5W	36

Table 6-2. Historically significant patented claims of the Rich Hill district.

Figure 6-5. Modern Octave sign.

Figure 6-6. Octave Mine in the late 1890s. In the upper left corner is the #2 shaft and headframe. The mill, below and to the right, was connected to the shaft by an elevated wooden tramway. Open air cyanide leaching and settling tanks are below the mill.
(photo courtesy of Sharlot Hall Museum)

Figure 6-7. Horse-drawn side-dump ore carts at the Octave Mine. The headframe of the #2 shaft is to the right. (photo courtesy of Sharlot Hall Museum)

1895 and 1900 and sent to nearby mills for processing. About 1900 a mill consisting of a forty-stamp battery, and using a combination of mercury amalgamation, table concentrators, and cyanidation was built. Two oil-fired boilers provided the steam to power the mining and mill equipment. Between 1900 and 1905 the Octave lode was mined to a depth of over 2000 feet along the dip of the vein, and 2000 feet along the strike, producing gold and silver worth about $2,250,000 in the dollars of the time. The town of Octave sprang up on patented mining claims owned by the mine, producing the first relatively "safe" community in the district. This resulted in part from the location on company lands, creating a "company town" with professional miners and their families. A company store provided for the needs of the town, and miners were partially paid in company scrip that was redeemable only in the company store. While

Figure 6-8. Octave Mining Company scrip. (courtesy of Sharlot Hall Museum)

Figure 6-9. Octave Mine and townsite, circa 1905. Photo is looking toward the east side of Rich Hill. White sands in the creek are tailings from the Octave mill.
(photo courtesy of Sharlot Hall Museum)

this was a common procedure in many mining camps of the time, it was often unfair to miners who saw most of their pay go right back to the company for housing and food. On the brighter side, the company scrip kept some families from starving, as alcoholic miners could not use them to purchase alcohol.

The mine was sold in 1905 to a Chicago stockbroker due to the depletion of almost all of the economically mineable ore. To the west, the vein was cut by a large fault, and the Joker Fault displaced the vein to the east. Below the 2000-foot level, the vein was reportedly over 4 feet wide but low grade. However there were insufficient funds to perform adequate exploration and development work, and the mine was sold.

In 1907 the mine was bought by a larger company, which erected an electric power plant at Wickenburg and ran eleven miles of transmission lines to provide power for the mine and mill. There were also "frantic and unintelligent efforts to recover the vein [beyond] the Joker [Fault]." The company did little else with the property, and produced almost no gold, closing the mine in 1912.

Figure 6-10. Cowboys at Stanton, Arizona, circa 1922.
(photo courtesy of Sharlot Hall Museum)

The Octave Mines Company was organized in 1918 under the direction of H. C. Gibbs of Boston and Donald S. Leas of Philadelphia. The company hired J. Nelson Nevius, Wilbur H. Grant, and Mr. Miller as mine engineers. Nevius reported in 1921 that

> the Octave Mine is an object lesson, showing that a mine may be abandoned before it is exhausted. When I first saw it the mine was a mess, both underground and on the surface. The conditions were such that to the west, the prospect was hopeless because the vein is cut by a profound fault at the base of the mountain. Someone had sunk a shaft said to be nearly 400 feet deep and failed to get below the loose material of the wash. The bottom of the mine was not accessible because the mine was filled with water to about the 800-foot level… The evidence underground, a mill-bin a third full of waste, and correspondence left at the office tell the tale of the wrecking of a good mining enterprise.

This company redeveloped the Joker Shaft, a set of tunnels on the northeastern back-side of Weaver Mountain on the Octave vein, which intersected the ore body with depth. After careful geologic detective work, Nevius directed heroic "double-Jack" hand-drilling operations that eventually found the displaced vein on the other side of

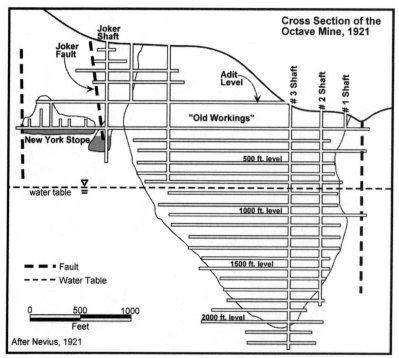

Figure 6-11. A cross-sectional view in the plane of the Octave vein from 1921. The "Old Workings" ore body is shown as the solid line. Over half of the "Old Workings" are below the water table. The Joker Workings to the left show where the ore body was rediscovered by J. N. Nevius. The gray areas around the New York Stope show ore mined just before the workings were mapped in 1921.

the Joker Fault. The vein was initially recovered on the 850-foot level of the Joker Shaft, which corresponds to the 250-foot level of the older mine workings. In his July 23, 1921, report, Nevius reported that

> a peculiar situation existed in that the evidence on the surface indicated a displacement of about 200 feet to the left, where a strong vein shows near the top of the ridge, but the evidence underground equally strongly indicates a displacement to the right. As the effects of the faulting were diminishing with depth, the 850-foot level was selected and the vein was recovered at the first attempt, the displacement being 50 feet to the right. More recent work has given some evidence of the existence at this point of two parallel veins about 50 feet apart, and the Joker Fault ends—like a tear part-way through a sheet of paper—at about this level. As exposed in the Joker Shaft, the vein shows a sudden wave just above the 1000-foot level, but no faulting occurs there, yet in the upper levels and on the surface the fault is unquestionable.

Nevius also identified ore zones in the Joker area called the "New York Stope" that contained over 25,000 ounces of gold. The "new" ore zones found in the displaced vein averaged about 1 ounce of gold and 2 ounces of silver per ton of ore, and were mined by various companies until 1939. With the fault-displaced section of the original vein relocated, operations in the old Octave workings recommenced as well.

Figure 6-12. Octave Mine circa 1937. The #3 shaft and headframe are to the left.
(photo courtesy of Sharlot Hall Museum)

Production from the Octave lode between 1895 and 1925 has been reported at about 53,000 ounces of gold and 75,000 ounces of silver, suggesting a lode gold purity of about 41% gold and 59% silver. Assay of old mine tailings and company records indicate that gold recovery after cyanide leaching was about 96%.

The Arizona Eastern Gold Mining Company was formed in 1928, and a 50-ton flotation mill was built to process ore from the Joker workings. Between 1928 and 1930, 9100 tons of ore were crushed, and sulfide minerals removed in the mill to produce a gold-rich concentrate. The concentrates were valued at $90,000 (1938 dollars), and contained roughly equal proportions of gold and silver.

The American Smelting and Refining Company (ASARCO) purchased the property in 1934, built a seven-mile pipeline from Antelope Spring to provide water, and modernized the mill. ASARCO operated the Joker workings from 1934 to 1941, and file data from the U.S. Bureau of Mines indicate that 48,694 tons of ore averaging 0.363 ounces of gold per ton, 0.464 ounces of silver per ton, 0.24% lead, and 0.03%

Figure 6-13. Interior of the Octave mill taken sometime in the 1930s. The stamp mills are behind the men and the amalgam shaker tables are to the front.
(photo courtesy of Sharlot Hall Museum)

Figure 6-14. Interior of the Octave Mine shop in the 1890s. Notice that all equipment on the shop floor is powered by belt-drive from a roof-mounted drive shaft. The drive shaft was probably driven by a steam engine located outside the shop.
(photo courtesy of Sharlot Hall Museum)

Figure 6-15. Octave Mine manager standing in front of the feed bins for the stamp mills. Ore shoveled into these bins would slowly feed into the mill by gravity to be crushed. (photo courtesy of Sharlot Hall Museum)

copper were mined. This corresponds to about 17,680 ounces of gold, 22,590 ounces of silver, and a gold purity of about 43%. In 1939 ASARCO was engaged in dewatering the original Octave Mine workings and the #3 shaft once again became a producer, but World War II terminated work.

The last recorded production by ASARCO was in 1942, and the mine officially closed in December. Little work was done at the Octave Mine following the war, with the exception of a few small parcels of select ore that were mined on contract in 1951. The property changed hands several times, and was razed along with the nearby town in the late 1950s. The mine later gained notoriety when it became the centerpiece of a platinum mining swindle in the 1980s. This swindle is described in more detail in chapter 9. At some point in the 1970's there was a minor cyanide-leaching operation that used thin plastic-lined open basins to re-treat tailings, though there is no record of any production from this operation. The remains of this operation are evident in the old tailings pile.

Figure 6-16. View of the Octave Mine #3 shaft in early 1950, with Rich Hill in the background. (photo courtesy of Arizona Division of Mines and Mineral Resources)

Figure 6-17. View of the Octave Mine and mill in early 1950, with Rich Hill in the background. (photo courtesy of Arizona Division of Mines and Mineral Resources)

Having produced about 80,000 ounces of gold, the Octave Mine remains by a substantial margin the single largest producer of lode gold from the Weaver District. In fact, the gold produced by the Octave even exceeds the official estimates of placer gold production for the entire district, though as noted before these estimates are clearly well below the actual placer gold production.

Figure 6-18. Map of the east end workings of the Octave Mine. Gray areas are workings excavated by ASARCO in 1936. The workings are inclined to the northwest, following the dip of the Octave vein.

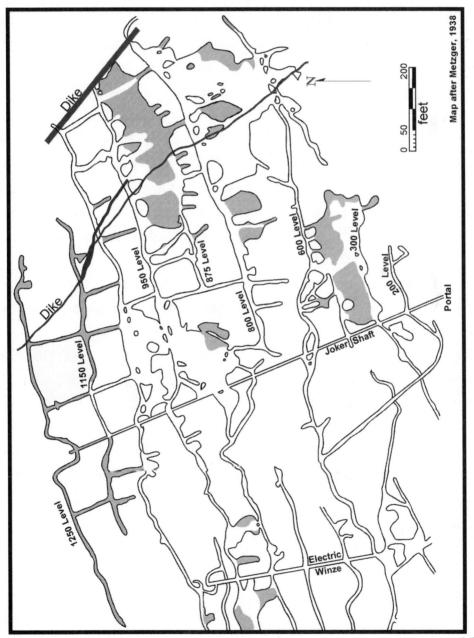

The workings of the Octave Mine consist of the main mine (Octave) and the adjacent Joker workings, which both mine the same ore body. The old Octave workings consist of a decline about 2000 feet deep, three shafts, and several thousand feet of tunnels. There are extensive stopes where ore was removed, centered upon three main zones of high-grade ore. The Joker workings consist of a shaft 1250 feet deep and about 3000 feet of tunnels. Most ore production was from below the 300-foot level of the mine, and within 800 feet of the shaft. The Joker workings are now the site of a sizable bat colony, which can be seen to emerge en mass at dusk.

The geology of the Octave Mine can be expressed quite simply: A quartz-gold vein is hosted within older granite and diorite. In more detail, the Octave vein dips at an angle of about 20° to 30° to the northwest, and strikes (runs) 70° east of north. The vein has experienced some degree of reverse faulting, as indicated by fault gouge and cleavage in the rock. Old faults have also displaced the eastern side of the vein to a depth of over 400 feet below the deep sediments of Weaver Creek. To the west, the vein has also been cut by old faults, but these faults (like the Joker) only offset the vein by 50 feet or so. The vein is traceable on the surface for at least 2500 feet of strike. A few small barren quartz veins cut the Octave vein, and are offset by the fault, indicating displacement of less than 100 feet. The richest ore in the vein occurs where it lies adjacent to and bounded by one of the Apache Diabase Dikes.

The Octave vein ranges from 5 inches to 5 feet thick, and averages about 3 feet thick. The vein consists of massive gray to white quartz, with rare disseminations (4% to 5%) of pyrite and galena. Older reports of the ore indicate that small amounts of chalcopyrite may also be present. All the sulfide minerals listed occur as disseminations, bands, and irregular masses. Little gold occurs as native gold (free gold), with most being microscopic inclusions on and within the sulfide minerals. J. N. Nevius stated that no coarse gold in quartz was ever found in the operations at Octave, though some small samples with small spots of native gold were reported to have been recovered on rare occasions during the early days of mining. Nevius also commented on the unusual occurrence of large coarse gold nuggets in the alluvial deposits around Octave, but scant native gold in the lode deposit. The pure galena assays 100 ounces of gold and silver per ton, while the pyrite averages 8 to 25 ounces per ton, and the chalcopyrite just 3 ½ to 7 ounces per ton. An assay by the authors on a specimen of quartz rich in galena yielded 10 ounces of gold per ton, and 20 ounces of silver per ton. Electron microprobe analyses by the authors of the same Octave galena ore

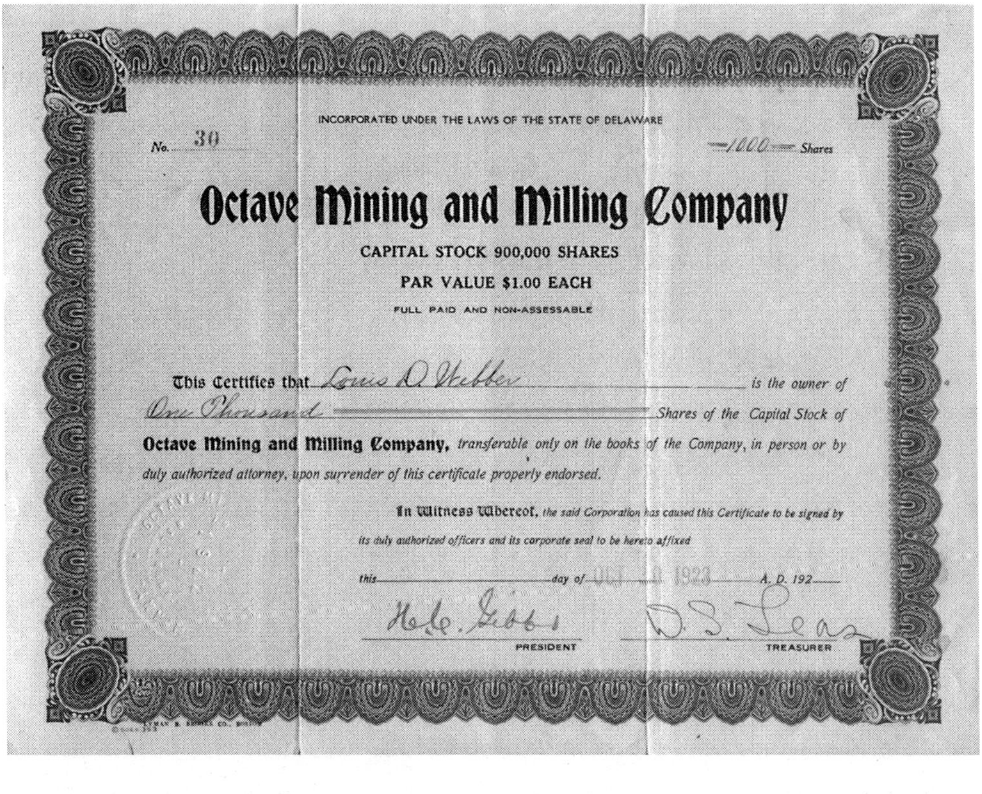

Figure 6-19. Stock certificates for the Octave Mine from two different eras.

showed a complex minerology. "Gold" occurs as 0.5 to 5 micron blebs, with an average purity of 84% (16% silver). Silver occurs as silver sulfide (argentite), native silver, silver-rich galena, and rare silver iodide. A band of faintly bluish-gray quartz up to a foot thick marks the bottom edge of the vein. Rock adjacent to the vein has been slightly altered, contains clay (sericite), and is often silicified. This alteration of adjacent rock allowed miners to break ore cleanly from the vein.

The Johnson Mine

This mine is probably the oldest lode mine in the district, perhaps sharing that honor with Charles Stanton's Leviathan Mine. An 1899 report to the territorial governor states that the mine "was worked for many years by the hermit Johnson, whose bones now lie buried under an immense wall of the lode from which he was stoping ore."

The author of that report also stated that a 4-ounce specimen of gold on quartz was purchased from Charles Stanton prior to 1886, and shown to William Johnson, who "recognized it as one of the specimens taken from his vein." Examination of court records in the collections of the Sharlot Hall Museum show that Johnson ended up taking Stanton to court over the same gold specimen. According to sworn court testimony, William Johnson claimed that Stanton came around his mine while he was working underground. When Johnson caught him snooping around, Stanton claimed that he wanted to borrow some tools for doing assessment work on the Leviathan Mine. Johnson states that this was doubtful, because Stanton knew little about mining and was averse to manual labor. Later, Johnson discovered that his prized gold specimen was missing from its hiding place. Johnson provided many corroborating witnesses and character references, and included the scathing comment that "this could be further supported by Timmerman...if he was still alive," which was clearly aimed at refreshing the judge's memory that Stanton was a prime suspect in Timmerman's murder. Stanton produced several character witnesses in his own defense, all of whom were likely paid for their testimony, or were his known accomplices in other crimes. One of Stanton's "hired witnesses" was an unemployed miner who provided ample arguments that while the gold certainly appeared to be from Johnson's mine in character, there was no way to conclusively prove that it did indeed come from that mine.

The judge ultimately ruled against Johnson. Within a year, the veteran miner Johnson was dead from an unexplained cave-in of his mine. Perhaps, like so many others, he was the victim of Stanton's vengeful ways.

The Johnson Mine was most likely opened in the mid- to late 1870s based upon the original paperwork filed for patenting of the Commodore and Homestake claims upon which the mine is located. Johnson hand-mined select high-grade ore by under-hand stoping from a 200-foot-deep inclined shaft that followed the dipping vein. Ore was processed in two horse-drawn arastras and amalgamated with mercury to re-cover gold. The cave-in that killed Johnson was in this portion of the mine, and he is still entombed there.

Following the death of Johnson, the mine lay idle for several years as his heirs lived on the East Coast and had no interest in mining. In 1894 the property was leased or sold to T. A. Conlee who opened a new tunnel on the vein where it was up to 6 feet thick. This section was mined for a few years, and yielded high-grade pockets of gold-bearing pyrite ore up to 3 feet thick. The average grade of ore from Conlee's operation was about ½ ounce of gold per ton of ore. In the late 1890s the site was owned by the Hamilton family and J. W. Smith. The mine claims were patented in 1898 and 1899.

In the 1930s, J. W. Smith floated a more elaborate mining scheme, and Johnson Gold Mines Inc. was formed. A 470-foot-deep inclined shaft was sunk to exploit the vein in conjunction with the renovated tunnel used by Conlee in 1894. Stopes on five levels advanced out from the shaft, exposing a payable high-grade ore zone 1 to 2 feet thick. When advancing the workings, compressed air jackhammers were used to drill eleven holes, each 4 feet deep. Ten holes would be loaded with explosives to break the rock, while the eleventh was left empty as a void for the explosives to "break" in to. Over 1500 feet of workings were developed in the mine. Ore was removed from stopes that were mined on 35-foot centers, and backfilled with waste rock. Local

Figure 6-20. William Johnson's signature from Yavapai County court records. (courtesy Sharlot Hall Museum)

timber was used in the mine, though a 1938 report states "almost any available scrap material is satisfactory [for timbering]." In 1936 about 20 tons of ore per day were produced from the mine, including a small amount quarried from the vein on the surface. In that same year, the mine employed seventeen men: ten miners, three mill workers, one hoistman, one timberman, one ore cart trammer (paid on contract), and one foreman, who also doubled as blacksmith. Pay was $4 to $5 per day, depending upon skill. Housing was provided in a bunkhouse at the mine.

A one-ton ore skip (elevator) was used to haul ore from the #2, #3, #4, and #5 levels to the underground ore pockets, while ore from the #1 level was moved by gravity down to the ore pockets. An ore pocket is simply a large vertical cavity in the mine that is used for intermediate storage of ore. The old Conlee tunnel, which is at the bottom of the ore pockets was rebuilt to serve as a haulage level. An iron ore chute door at the bottom of an ore pocket would be opened to allow ore to fall into a waiting ore cart. The door was then closed, and the ore cart pushed out of the tunnel to the mill for processing. This "short cut" eliminated the expense of hauling ore all the way out of the mine using the skip. A contract worker, who was paid 10¢ per cart, pushed the ½-ton ore carts out of the mine.

The Johnson mill had a capacity to process up to 50 tons of ore per day. Ore from the mine was dumped into one of two 50-ton capacity ore bins, from which it was fed into a 10 inch by 2 inch jaw crusher. The gravel-sized particles that came out of the jaw crusher were fed into a 4 foot by 5 foot ball mill to reduce the ore to sand-sized particles. A hydraulic separator and a Deister vibrating sand table were used to produce a concentrate of heavy minerals, including some native gold. The tailings off the Deister table were processed by froth flotation to recover sulfide minerals such as the gold-bearing pyrite and galena. Gravity concentrates contained over 15 ounces of gold and 3 ounces of silver per ton, while flotation concentrates averaged 4 ounces of gold and 4 ounces of silver to the ton. These concentrates were processed by amalgamation in an 18 inch by 36 inch amalgamation pan. Retorting of the gold- and silver-rich mercury was performed once a week under the watchful eye of the foreman. In later years the concentrates were sent directly to smelters in other parts of Arizona. The mine produced about 3000 gallons of water each day in the lower workings, and this water was pumped out and used in the mill. In 1940 the mine was sold to MacMillan

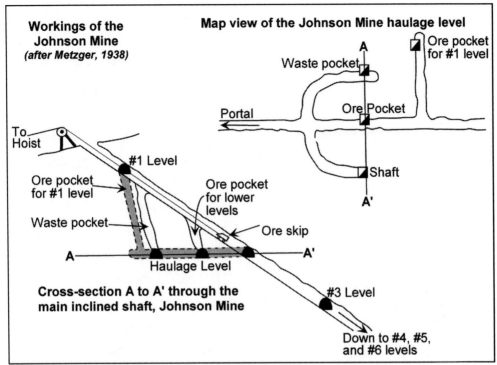

Figure 6-21. Workings of the Johnson Mine. In the upper right is a map view of the main haulage level of the mine, showing locations of the shaft and pockets used for underground storage of ore and waste rock (diagonal-filled boxes). Rock would be hauled from lower levels by the skip, and dumped into the top of the pocket. When needed, a mine cart would be placed under the chute at the bottom of the pocket, which would be opened to fill the cart with rock. The cart would then be pushed out of the mine through the haulage level. Line A-A' indicates the line of the cross-sectional view of the mine shown in the lower left. Gray areas are tunnels running parallel behind the plane of the cross-section, while black areas show tunnels that run perpendicular to the page.

Oil Company, which briefly tried to mine the vein. When mining was halted at the start of World War II, the pumps were turned off, and the workings filled with water to about 50 feet below the haulage level.

Following World War II, the mine was sold to, and sporadically operated by, Frank and E. G. Russell. During this time the mine became informally known as the "Russell Mine." Operations from the late 1940s to early 1960s were limited to stoping of small quantities of remnant ore from the existing mine above the water table.

In 1975 Bill Dean and Dave Galloway formed the Precious Metals Mining Company, which sunk a 175-foot-deep inclined shaft, and drove a 70-foot adit into the vein. Significant tonnages of payable ore were not found, and the company suspended operations in 1976.

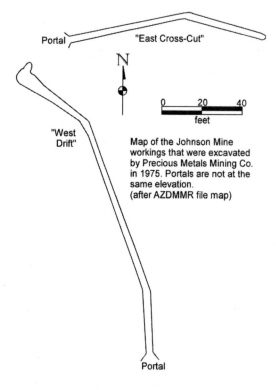

Portal

"East Cross-Cut"

N

0   20   40
feet

"West
Drift"

Map of the Johnson Mine
workings that were excavated
by Precious Metals Mining Co.
in 1975. Portals are not at the
same elevation.
(after AZDMMR file map)

Portal

Figure 6-22. Map view of the mine workings excavated by the Precious Metals Mining Company in 1975 at the Johnson Mine. While these tunnels cut several veins, none proved rich enough to warrant further mining operations, and the company ceased operations the following year. Note that the portals are not at the same elevation, and workings cut the vein from different sides, at different elevations.

The vein of the Johnson Mine is 1½ to 6 feet thick and at least 300 feet long. This vein trends to the northeast, and dips 29° to the northwest. Mineralization of the vein is quartz with lenses of gold-bearing pyrite up to 3 feet thick. Minor pods of gold-bearing galena and sphalerite are also present. An unusual aspect of the upper levels of the Johnson Mine is the occurrence of the masses of native gold that were noted in the 1894 and 1930s operations. The specimen reported in the 1899 governor's report, and the fact that Johnson was able to process his ore by simple crushing and amalgamation also suggest that free-milling gold was common in the weathered upper portion of the vein. This occurrence of significant quantities of native gold is unusual for the lode deposits of the Weaver District, and probably is the main reason that it was among the first veins to be mined.

Workings at the mine site consist of the 200-foot caved-in inclined shaft of the original Johnson Mine, the 470-foot adit from the 1894 operations, an inclined shaft and workings from the 1930s, and the 175-foot shaft and 70-foot adit from 1975. There are also two 50-foot inclined shafts and numerous prospect pits of unknown age.

The Leviathan Mine

Records show that Dennis May, who had discovered the Congress gold mine north of Wickenburg, had filed the original claim on the Leviathan. The claims include the Leviathan, Denver, Chester, Grantly, and Germanic. May was also an employee of the Vulture Mine, where Charles Stanton was the assay officer and Sexton White was the mine manager. Stanton and White convinced May that it was not necessary to complete his yearly assessment on the Leviathan claim. When the claim ownership lapsed due to this lack of activity, Stanton and Sexton filed for ownership and were granted the claim on the mine shortly thereafter.

A year after the claim was filed, Sexton disappeared with all the gold and back pay from the Vulture Mine safe and was never heard from again. Stanton moved to Rich Hill when his old boss disappeared, and among other ventures tried to open the Leviathan deposit as a mine. While workers hired to perform the obligatory exploration work apparently produced several flashy specimens, the shallow prospects excavated at this time did not produce commercial amounts of gold. Stanton had a bad reputation because of his association with several "salted" mines. Yavapai County court records as well as the 1899 report to the governor suggest that some Leviathan samples possessed by Stanton were actually "highgraded" from the Johnson Mine. Not much is known about the early days of the Leviathan Mine due to Stanton's secretive nature and premature death. In keeping with government efficiency of the times, the formal patent of ownership on the Leviathan (mineral patent #12906) was granted to Charles Stanton on March 3, 1888—almost two years after Stanton's death!

In 1934 Chase Rich and others bought the property from a Mr. Maximillion, and began the first serious mining. Between 1934 and 1941 the mine produced an amount of gold and silver "comparable to the Myers Mine" from 2000 feet of workings, including a 250-foot main shaft with drifts, and 12 other shallow shafts. Ore reportedly averaged ¼ ounce of gold to the ton, but one worker recalls a rich pocket of specimens that "filled a 5 gallon bucket, and yielded $500 [25 ounces] in gold." The mine closed operations just prior to the outbreak of World War II. Since this time, the mine has lain idle, though between 1984 and 1986 Los Suertes Mining Corporation of Scottsdale, Arizona, conducted an electromagnetic geophysical study of the site and drilled 2000 feet of exploratory core drilling.

The vein is about 2000 feet long, striking about 50° east of north, and dipping 40° to the northwest. At its maximum the vein is 12 feet thick, but averages only 3 feet thick. The vein is paralleled by dikes of diabase, and consists of quartz with gold- and silver-bearing galena and chalcopyrite.

Mountainside Mine

This mine was staked and claimed on February 7, 1897, by a young mining engineer named George Upton. The rock in the 250-foot shaft was promising enough that in 1898 a small pilot mill was built on the site. This mill consisted of a two-stamp battery, sulfide flotation cells, and mercury amalgamation drums. Cyanide leaching tanks were installed a few years later. Upton purchased adjoining claims in 1898 and 1899. The Mountainside Mine at this time included the Mountaineer, Golden Mountainside, Mountaintop, Northend, and Mamie claims. An 1100-foot tunnel was driven to connect the mine with the 400-foot shaft on the Mamie claim. A 140-foot-deep shaft was also sunk on the Northend claim. About 500 tons of ore were milled from these workings between 1898 and 1934, and several small shipments of high-grade galena-pyrite ore were shipped directly to the smelter in Globe, Arizona. The ore averaged about 1.5 ounces of gold per ton, and 1.5 ounces of silver per ton. The mine produced about 800 ounces of gold during this period.

Figure 6-23. Stock certificate from the Mountainside Mine.

As Upton grew older and became unable to work the mine by himself, he and his niece Maurine Sanborn tried to sell the mine. In 1941 the Mountainside Mine was offered for sale at $80,000, or on lease for 15% royalty. Upton, an experienced mine engineer, claimed that the deposit still contained 175,000 tons of ore grading 1 ¼ ounce of gold per ton.

In 1983 Al Wittliff cleaned out the old workings of the Mountainside Mine and re-timbered. A tunnel was extended on two gold-rich veins, and a small quantity of select hand-sorted ore was processed on-site using a jaw crusher, ball mill, and gravity table. A few tons were processed, yielding about 1 ounce of gold per ton.

The Mountainside vein averages 2½ feet thick, and dips 42° to the north. A dike (layer) of dark rock parallels the vein, and was believed by Upton to be related to the formation of the deposit. The mineralization of the vein consists of quartz with gold-bearing galena and pyrite.

Dixie-Rincon Mine

The Dixie-Rincon Mine dates back to about 1880, when exploration work for the adjoining Marcus Mine disclosed the Dixie-Rincon veins. The Marcus Mine, which lies just to the west of the Dixie-Rincon produced about 4000 ounces of gold and silver between 1880 and 1902. The ore from the Marcus must have been exceptionally rich as records indicate that it was hauled 100 miles by wagon to the Southern Pacific railhead, then shipped to a smelter in Newark, New Jersey.

The Dixie-Rincon Mine worked ore from two main veins, the Welcome and Dixie. The Welcome vein is nearly vertical, and consists of quartz with gold-rich pyrite. The vein is at least 5500 feet long and up to 50 feet thick, though economic mineralization is restricted to a zone of pyrite-rich rock about a foot thick. The Dixie vein is a quartz vein with gold-rich galena and pyrite, and is about 3300 feet long. The Dixie vein dips 22° to the northwest and averages 14 inches thick. Cross-cutting relationships indicate that the Dixie vein is older than the Welcome vein. Smaller veins on the property include the Upper Dixie, South Welcome, and Marcus.

From 1904 to 1907 the Rincon Gold Mining Company, under the direction of Thomas G. Hunter, produced over 2000 ounces of gold and 1000 ounces of silver along with an appreciable amount of lead from the property. The exact amount of metals produced during this period is unknown as most of the smelter records were lost when the smelter went bankrupt. The main workings were the Dixie shaft, an inclined 1058-foot-deep single compartment shaft with over 3700 feet of stopes and drifts on the vein with levels at 100-foot intervals. Ore averaged about 1 ounce of gold and 1 ounce of silver per ton. The ore was milled on-site to produce a rough concentrate that averaged almost 7 ounces of gold and 6 ounces of silver per ton, and yielded 9% lead and 31% iron. These concentrates were shipped to the Humboldt smelter for final processing and refining. In addition, this same period saw exploration of the Welcome vein with the sinking of the Main Welcome shaft (165 feet deep), the Willard shaft (60 feet deep), and the Hibbard shaft (40 feet deep).

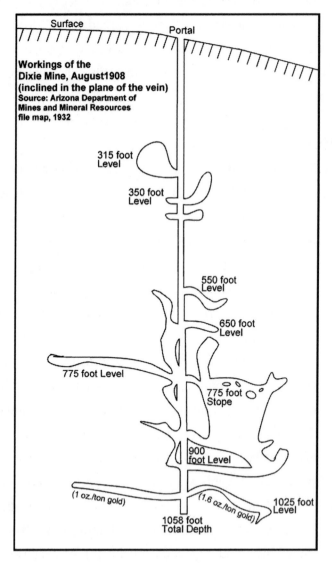

Figure 6-24. Workings of the Dixie-Rincon Mine, circa 1908.

Figure 6-25. Stock certificate from the Rincon Mine.

The Humboldt smelter went bankrupt in late 1907, and a considerable amount of concentrates shipped by the Rincon Gold Mining Company were never paid for. This put the Rincon Mine in serious financial straights. Between 1908 and 1910 the company tried to extricate itself from dire financial trouble by producing several railcar loads of rich concentrates that were up to 10 ounces of gold per ton, but these efforts were not enough to satisfy the creditors and the mine closed in late 1910. For the next two decades, legal and financial complications conspired to keep the mine closed.

In 1934 George Spear operated the mine under lease. Spear mined both oxide and sulfide ore from the Genung shaft, which was located about 300 feet east of the Dixie shaft. All of the ore was scavenged from the old surface dumps, or from the upper 30 feet of the Genung shaft. On December 22, 1934, he shipped 4 tons of hand-sorted ore that yielded a total of 12 ounces of gold and 11 ounces of silver. A second shipment of 4 tons of unsorted ore was sent in January 1935, and yielded 5 ounces of gold and 5 ounces of silver. At the same time that Spear was leasing the mine, Don C. Hibbert had negotiated a lease on the old mine dumps of the South

Welcome and Marcus. A bulk shipment of 37 tons of this dump material went to the Magma smelter in Superior, Arizona. The shipment averaged only 0.41 ounces of gold to the ton, yielding 15 ounces of gold. After costs of shipping and smelting were deducted, Mr. Hibbert netted only $283 for his troubles.

Between 1937 and 1939 the Rincon Holdings Company, under the management of W. B. Smith and J. C. Lovett dewatered the Dixie shaft to the 500-foot level. Consultants filed several reports on the property. On July 27, 1938, 42 tons of ore were shipped to the Phelps Dodge smelter in Jerome, Arizona. This lot of ore averaged 1 ounce of gold and 1.3 ounces of silver per ton, and netted 42 ounces of gold and 54 ounces of silver. Another shipment of 33 tons to the same smelter on September 26 of the same year yielded 32 ounces of gold and 31 ounces of silver, and ran 0.11% copper. A final shipment of 33 tons was sent in January of 1939 to the smelter at Superior, Arizona, and produced 16 ounces of gold and 34 ounces of silver.

In early June of 1940, Ed Paul leased the mine and extracted 24 tons of higher-grade ore from the Genung and Rincon shafts. This unsorted ore averaged ½ ounce of gold and 1 ounce of silver to the ton. This ore was shipped through the Wickenburg Ore Market to the smelter at Hayden, Arizona, and yielded 12 ounces of gold, and 24 ounces of silver. In late June, a much smaller parcel of lower-grade ore was also shipped. In December of 1940 Earl Thomason took over the lease and shipped 5 tons of ore through the Wickenburg Ore Market. This shipment yielded 5 ounces each of gold and silver. The mine was shut down for World War II, and there is no record of any further official production from the mine.

Devil's Nest Mine

The Devil's Nest Mine consists of both lode and placer claims. The lode deposit consists of several 3- to 8-inch-wide quartz veins that are typical of the district. The placer deposits are eluvial and alluvial material that has eroded off of Rich Hill. Some of this sediment was reworked long ago by ancient creeks, producing gold-rich "Red Placers." These paleo-placers were dissected by modern Weaver Creek and other smaller tributaries, leaving sections of rich reddish gravels stranded high up in the bank walls. A large percentage of the gravels were reworked by drywashers in the early days of the district.

In 1931, George Thomason, father of Clyde Thomason (see chapter 8), filed placer claims for the Lucky Roxie and part of the Wild Horse block of claims. Results must have been encouraging, as a water well was drilled and the remaining Wild Horse claims were purchased in 1939, followed by the "400" property in 1945, and the Rock House in 1946. Avoiding the problems experienced by early miners who used drywashers, Thomason processed his gravels by hydraulic methods, using water from his well.

By 1961 the property was owned by a man named Frederickson, who built an elaborate drywashing plant that was capable of processing 175 cubic yards of gravels per day. Unfortunately for Frederickson, he encountered the same problems that hindered his predecessors who tried drywashing in this area. The gravels were just too wet and "clumpy" for drywashing to work effectively, even at shallow depths. Between 1961 and 1963 there were several modifications made to the drywashing plant, but all proved ineffective or too costly.

In the early 1970s, Vivian Hale owned the fourteen placer and lode claims. Together with Bruce Allen, they claimed to have found a shear zone in the schist bedrock that was 40 feet wide and reportedly contained an amazing 31 ounces of gold per ton, 11 ounces of platinum per ton, and 21 ounces of palladium per ton. A shear zone of this size would be exceptional for the Weaver District, and the reporting of unusual platinum and palladium mineralization raised quite a few eyebrows in the local mining community. In early 1973 the Arizona Division of Mines and Mineral Resources investigated the reported lode claims with the owners. The result was a determination that the shear zone was misidentified, and that absolutely no detectable amount of platinum or palladium was present in the rocks. Even though this claim of platinum and palladium at the Devil's Nest Mine was discounted, the seeds had been planted for a later swindle at the Octave Mine in the 1970s.

By late 1973 the mine was owned by Jim Sweeney, who took an interest in the more tangible, but low-grade, gold lode deposits. Operations consisted of surface mining of a 4-inch-wide quartz vein. The ore was hand quarried, sorted, and hand crushed. Crushed ore was processed on a vibrating gravity table to recover gold. A visit by a geologist from Arizona Division of Mines and Mineral Resources noted that the vein contained 0.05 to 0.1 ounces of gold per ton, and that limonite mineralized rock from the vein could be crushed and panned to yield visible gold. A small hydraulic dredge and sluice was also used to process placer gravels.

By 1976 Jim Sweeney and his partner, Mr. Schleisman, had given up on lode mining, and were operating a 4 foot by 24 foot trommel to process 40 to 50 cubic yards of gravels per day. Gravels were being mined to bedrock at a depth of 8 feet, and the gravels were reported to average over a gram of gold to the yard.

The Jackpot Mining Company tested and evaluated the Devil's Nest claims between 1983 and 1987, and finally purchased them in 1987. The Jackpot Mining Company later changed its name to Yavapai Mining Company.

16-to-1 Mine

Also known as the Schoonover Mine, the 16-to-1 deposit consists of a gold-rich quartz vein 4 to 5 feet thick, striking 15° east of north, and dipping 30° to 35° to the west. The vein was mined in the 1920s and 1930s from a main tunnel with several stopes, raises, and winzes. Henry "Buck" Schoonover, a one-legged miner who lived in his tunnel, operated the mine during the 1920s and 1930s. There are several other prospect workings nearby. The amount of gold mined, and the grade of ore is not known, but estimates based upon the size of the stopes and average ore grade in the district suggest production of at least 100 ounces of gold. In 1973 Carl Carlson purchased the mine, though there is no record of any mining at this time. This mine was later sold to Eugene Chaney, and in 1981 was listed among other properties he was "promoting" as part of the "Octave Swindle" (which is discussed in chapter 9).

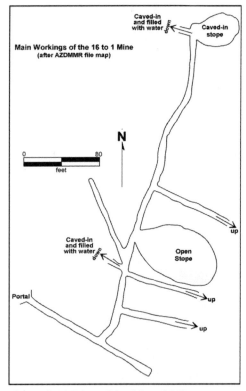

Figure 6-26. Map of the 16-to-1 Mine.

Table 6-3. Summary of the production histories of the most important mines in the Rich Hill area.

Name	Metals in deposit (bold = economically important)	Development Status	Year Discovered	First Year of Recorded Production	Last Year of Recorded Production	*Estimated Production
16 to 1	Au	Intermittent Producer	pre-1900s	1920s	1930s	at least 100 oz. gold; no reported silver
Beehive	Au	Developed Producer	pre-1890s	1918	1941	over 1,500 oz. gold; no reported silver
Blue Ball	Au Cu Ag Pb	Prospect	pre-1960	---	---	Unknown
Box Placer	Au	Prospect	pre-1960	---	---	Unknown
De Vault Placer	Au	Prospect	pre-1960	---	---	Unknown
Desert Gold	Au	Prospect	pre-1970	---	---	Unknown
Devil's Nest	Au	Intermittent Producer	1860s	1931	---	Unknown
Dixie-Rincon	Au **Pb** Cu	Intermittent Producer	1880	1906	1936	over 2,300 oz. gold; 1,300 oz. silver
Dos Caballeros	Au	Prospect	pre-1970	---	---	Unknown
Endependence	Au Ag Cu	Intermittent Producer	1910	1913	1838	over 200 oz. gold; 250 oz. silver
Golden Goose	Au	Intermittent Producer	1860s	---	---	"goose egg-sized nuggets"
Golden Gravel	Au	Prospect	pre-1970	---	---	Unknown
Gray Fox	W	Intermittent Producer	1952	1952	1954	180 lbs. of WO₃
Grey Mare	Au	Prospect	pre-1970	---	---	Unknown
Hackberry Lode	Au	Prospect	pre-1970	---	---	Unknown
Hayden	Au	Intermittent Producer	1895	1895	1940	over 50 oz. gold; 30 oz. silver
Helen Morris	Au	Prospect	pre-1890s	1946	1946	16 oz. gold; no reported silver
Jerome	Au	Intermittent Producer	1891	1892	1942	less than 100 oz. gold; no reported silver
John Sloan	Au Cu Ag Pb	Prospect	pre-1900s	---	---	Unknown
Johnson	Au **Pb**	Developed Producer	1870s	1880s	1942	over 1,000 oz. gold; 1,500 oz. silver
Laurella	Au Ag Cu Pb Zn	Intermittent Producer	1907	1936	1939	85 oz. gold; 61 oz. silver
Leviathan	Au Ag Cu	Developed Producer	1870	1934	1941	about 750 oz. gold; no reported silver
Lucky Johnnie	Au Ag Cu	Prospect	pre-1930s	---	---	less than 10 oz. gold; no reported silver
Merrill Placer	Au	Prospect	pre-1960	1930s	1930s	Unknown
Mesa Grande	W	Intermittent Producer	1963	1953	1958	150 lbs. of WO₃
Meyers	Au Ag Cu Pb Zn	Developed Producer	pre-1920s	1934	1947	about 800 oz. gold; no reported silver
Mizpah	Au	Intermittent Producer	pre-1900	1910s	1930s	at least 200 oz. gold; no reported silver
Montana King	Au	Prospect	---	---	---	Unknown
Mountainside	Au Ag	Intermittent Producer	1897	1898	1983	about 850 oz. gold; 800 oz. silver
Octave	Au Ag	Developed Producer	1865	1895	1951	about 80,000 oz. gold; 80,000 oz. silver
Pyramid	Fe Ti **Mn** P S Si	Prospect	1942	1942	---	Unknown
Rattlesnake Haven	Au	Prospect	pre-1970	---	---	Unknown
Red Metal	Au	Intermittent Producer	pre-1900	---	---	Unknown
Red Twister	Au	Intermittent Producer	pre-1900	1910	1920s	at least 150 oz. gold; 200 oz. silver
Reese Mine	Au	Intermittent Producer	pre-1970	---	---	Unknown
Shaft #4	Au	Prospect	pre-1940	---	---	Unknown
Shaft #3	Au	Prospect	pre-1940	---	---	Unknown
Upton Placer	Au	Prospect	1946	---	---	Unknown
War Eagle	Au	Prospect	1939	1939	1946	less than 20 oz. gold; no reported silver
Wildhorse Placer	Au	Intermittent Producer	pre-1970	---	---	Unknown
Wright	Au	Prospect	pre-1970	---	---	Unknown
Yarnell	Au Ag **Pb** Cu Zn	Intermittent Producer	pre-1890s	1914	1941	over 4,000 oz. gold; no reported silver
Yellowjacket	Au Ag **Pb** Cu Zn	Intermittent Producer	1905	1939	1959	less than 50 oz. gold; no reported silver

*Estimated production is based upon historical records, average ore grade, size of tailings pile, and size of stopes and workings.

101

Chapter 7

The Great Depression, World War II, and the End of an Era

(1928–1970)

Mining during the Great Depression

The Great Depression of 1928 to 1942 spurred a tremendous revival of placer gold mining in Arizona, and the Rich Hill area was no exception. During these hard economic times, $2 was considered a good day's pay, assuming that you could find work. With that in mind, many people across the nation began performing the following simple calculation:

> An average worker can process 10 cubic yards of gravel through a wet sluice in one day. Most "old timers" did not bother with placers averaging less than 0.05 ounces of gold per cubic yard, leaving virtually all the lower-grade placers untouched. Assuming that you could find placers averaging at least 0.01 ounces of gold per cubic yard, which should be easy, and with the price of gold at $20 per ounce:

$$(\$20 \text{ per oz.}) \times (0.01 \text{ oz. per yd}^3) \times (10 \text{ yd}^3 \text{ per day}) = \$2 \text{ per day!}$$

The U.S. government raised the price of gold to $35 per ounce on January 31, 1934, when it was realized that this could put thousands of people to work during the hard times. Low interest federal loan programs for individuals who wanted to start gold mines were also initiated. Virtually every placer district in Arizona, from Plomosa to Chase Creek was reworked during this time, and placer gold production in Arizona boomed. At the same time, many small operators and lessees attempted to work some of the hard rock mines of Rich Hill.

At Rich Hill there were many families and small groups of men who survived and even prospered by drywashing. Since water is

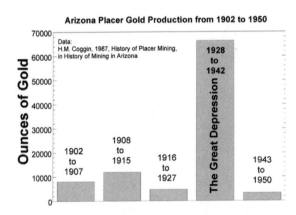

Figure 7-1. Arizona placer gold production.

Figure 7-2. Mother and son working the placers along Weaver Creek with a rocker in 1932. (photo courtesy of the *Engineering and Mining Journal*)

scarce in the area, drywashers and dry jigs were used as they could be easily constructed and left precious water resources for drinking (see Appendix A). In the wet months of the late summer and winter, it was sometimes possible to use sluices and rockers.

Much of the mining activity seems to have focused upon the thick low-grade gravels around the Decision Corner area and to the north, as the best areas were either under claim, or considered to be worked out. In the Decision Corner area there are numerous tin can dumps that date to the 1930s, many of which are overlying older garbage dumps. One such dump is located in Section 6 facing the Octave Mine, and exploration will reveal many interesting rusty items, as well as the low stone walls built up around the clapboard and tent structures of the camp. There are also several shallow shafts in the area that were sunk or re-opened in attempts to exploit buried "Red Placers." No evidence has been found that indicates whether these attempts were successful or not. About fifty men worked this lower portion of the field in the winter of 1932–33, with each averaging only about 0.15 ounces of gold per week due to their reworking of previously mined gravels and the low-grade placers. During that same winter, lucky individuals found several nuggets over three ounces in Weaver Creek, and two nuggets over five ounces from Antelope Creek.

Typical operations, if there was such a thing, consisted of one or two people to dig the *pay dirt* (gold-bearing placer gravels), one person to operate the drywasher, and one person to feed pay dirt into the washer and clean away the drywasher tailings and oversize material. The pay dirt would come from a variety of sources, including the modern stream channels and "Red Placers." Pay dirt would be excavated, and then screened to about 1 inch or less. Screening was often done with wire mesh on a wooden frame, though some would put the young children of the family to work screening pay dirt by hand. The drywashers that were used in the 1930s were essentially the same design as most modern drywashers (see Appendix A). Screened pay dirt would

Figure 7-4. A gasoline-powered drywash plant on lower Weaver Creek, 1932. Note the coarse oversize reject pile in front, and the fine rejects coming out of the chute on the left side. A plant of this size could handle several tons of dry dirt per day. The view is from Decision Corner to the northeast toward Weaver Mountain. (photo courtesy of the *Engineering and Mining Journal*)

be shoveled onto an upper *grizzly* that consisted of an inclined box covered with wire mesh or bars that allowed material smaller than 3/8 inch to pass through, while the larger oversize material would slide off to be discarded. The fines that passed through the grizzly would pour onto a second inclined box called the *washer box*. This hollow box had a cloth covering and cross-riffle bars. The significant departure from modern drywashers is that bellows were manually manipulated to force air through the hollow box. As the air passed through the cloth cover, the lighter material from the pay dirt would be blown away or slide off the inclined washer box, while heavier gold and black sands would remain trapped behind the riffle bars. Often the bellows would be rigged to jiggle the washer box during the operation, to enhance recovery of gold. When the riffles were full of black sand and gold, the washer box would be removed and the drywashed contents, called *concentrates*, were dumped into a large bucket for later processing. An industrious team of three could process up to 5 cubic yards of placer gravel in a day with a single drywasher. Another variation on the drywasher included the dry rocker cradle, though this and other crude devices were considerably less successful in recovering gold.

Figure 7-3. A small lever-operated bellows drywasher (left) and a hand-crank drywasher (right). These machines could at best process about two tons of dry-screened placer gravels in a day. Photos taken on the lower portion of Weaver Creek in 1932. (photo courtesy of the *Engineering and Mining Journal*)

Camps would often work for five to ten days drywashing pay dirt, before taking their drywashed concentrates to water for washing. As water was scarce in the Rich Hill area, and wells were rare, this often meant packing the concentrates eleven miles away to the Hassayampa River.

The final cleanup of the concentrates would involve carefully panning away less dense material and as much of the black sands as possible. The remaining gold and black sands could then be picked for the coarse gold. Fine gold would be recovered by drying the remaining concentrate in the sun or in a pan over a fire. The dried concentrates could then be processed with either a magnet to remove black sands, or by careful puffing by a person. The remaining gold would be handpicked from the black sands.

Larger placer operations did much better due to improved efficiencies of scale but many small companies were also formed. In 1938 the largest placer producer was the Thunderbird property in Oro Fino Gulch, operated by the Universal Placer Mining Corporation with a power shovel and large drywashing plant.

World War II, Public Law L-208, and the End of Sanctioned Mining

When Pearl Harbor was bombed in December of 1941, the country began a massive mobilization for the war effort, the scale of which was unprecedented in the nation's history. The pressing need for war materials as well as manpower for the

Figure 7-4. Testing Weaver Creek placer gravels in 1932 using a sluice and recirculation pump to conserve precious water. Samples being washed were from a test shaft nearby. View to the west toward the Devil's Nest mine and Rich Hill from the vicinity of Decision Corner. (photo courtesy of the *Engineering and Mining Journal*)

military and strategic industries resulted in the War Production Board issuing a law, WPB-L-208, on October 8, 1942. All gold mines in the United States were closed unless they also produced significant quantities of strategic minerals. This law closed all placer operations, as well as all hard rock mines in the Rich Hill area. The Yarnell Mine closed in September and the Octave Mine closed in December. The U.S. Geological Survey reported that only 56 ounces of placer gold were recovered in the Rich Hill area for the whole of 1942. Almost all male gold miners were inducted into the service, or transferred to Arizona mines that produced strategic minerals such as copper. Most would never return to the Rich Hill area, as they grew accustomed to the higher wages, job security, and higher quality of life offered in the company towns of Morenci and Bisbee.

At the same time as the closures, scrap iron was needed for the war effort, and the equipment at many abandoned gold mines and camps was picked over during scrap iron collection drives. In Arizona, much of the remaining equipment not melted down as scrap was relocated to the vital copper mines.

When public law WPB-L-208 was rescinded near the end of the war on July 1, 1945, the damage to the gold mining industry was significant. Prosperous times, a fixed government price of $35 per ounce for gold, and a lack of capital for the purchase of replacement equipment conspired to eliminate virtually all placer mining across the nation, and many of the marginally profitable hard rock lode mines as well. The Octave Mine remained closed, and the town of Octave, which once numbered about 5000, was now empty. Soon after the war, the entire town of Octave was leveled, leaving only stone foundations and cellar pits. The town of Stanton was almost empty, with the population limited to George Upton and his niece Maurine Sanborn. The difficult but rich dry placers at Rich Hill were largely abandoned to hopeful absentee claim holders and the few remaining "hobo miners" who were too poor to move away.

George Upton's Stanton

If longevity were a reason to name a town, Stanton should surely be named Upton. George B. Upton, a geological engineer, moved to Arizona from Iowa in 1895, and shortly thereafter purchased the entire town of Stanton and built a home. Upton prospected much of the area near Stanton, and developed both lode and placer claims with a group of Iowa investors. In addition to his Rich Hill District claims, Upton also developed the Oro Grande Mine near Wickenburg. He worked the Oro Grande from its discovery in 1901 until the mine closed in 1907. In 1907, Upton founded the Distillate Storage Company, a retail and wholesale oil company located in Wickenburg. Upton was active in the Wickenburg community, leading the fight for the town's incorporation and helping to win the routing of a state highway through town (Highway 89). In 1922, Upton sold the Distillate Storage Company (which had by that time been renamed the Upton Oil Company) to Standard Oil. Throughout the years that George Upton was engaged in business activities in Wickenburg he never lost interest in his Rich Hill claims or his home in Stanton. Stanton was George Upton's home, and he continued to live in Stanton until his death at age ninety-nine in 1962.

George Upton's niece, Maurine Sanborn came to live in Stanton in 1934 to help care for him and his wife, who died in 1935. Sanborn recalled that "during the years of the depression, Stanton was surrounded by tents. In them lived doctors, lawyers, persons of many professions, seeking a fortune by placer mining." She also recalled that "the gold was bought by traveling peddlers, who brought with them scales to measure it. There was a gentlemen's agreement which allowed a man to fill a baking powder can full of nuggets, after which he had to quit for the day."

With the end of the Great Depression, the start of the World War II, and the Mine Closure Act of 1942, gold mining in the Stanton area ceased. The town of Stanton was once again on its way to becoming a ghost town. Maurine Sanborn became the town's caretaker, doing her best to preserve both the 1860s Charles Stanton–era commercial buildings as well as the 1890s George Upton–era residential buildings.

By 1959, the upkeep of the ghost town became too much for Sanborn. She and Upton sold a ten-acre parcel that included the hotel, saloon, post office, and a house to the *Saturday Evening Post*. Two unusual stipulations were included in the contract of the sale. If any mining was done during Maurine Sanborn's lifetime, half of the proceeds would go to her. Also no alcoholic beverages could be sold on the premises during her lifetime. Shortly after Sanborn sold the town, a sonic boom did a great deal of damage to some of the older buildings.

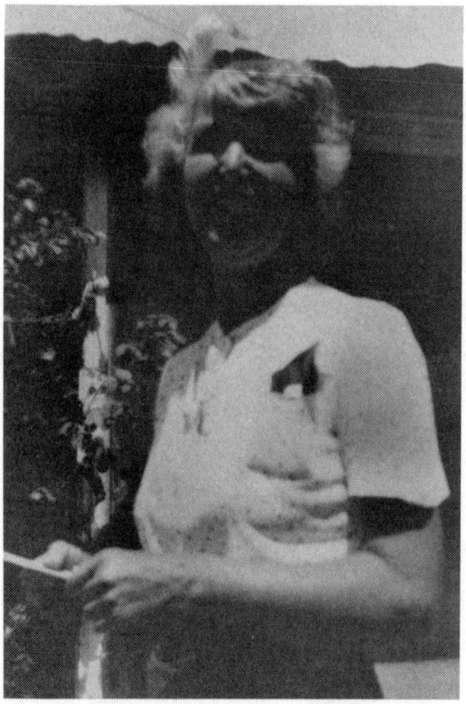

Figure 7-5. Maurine Sanborn at Stanton, Arizona, during the 1950s. (courtesy of Sharlot Hall Museum)

The *Saturday Evening Post* used Stanton as the prize in a contest. Stanton, renamed Ulcer Gulch, was offered as a prize to "the person in the advertising business who wrote the best ending to a jingle indicating that it pays to advertise in *The Post*."

The winner of the contest was Anne Foster of the J. Walter Thompson Agency in New York, New York. The story of winning a ghost town (Stanton) in a contest also inspired Clarence Budington Kelland to write a seven-installment story entitled "The Secret of Sidewinder Gulch" that appeared in the *Saturday Evening Post* during June and July of 1960. As of the fourth installment of "The Secret of Sidewinder Gulch," Ms. Foster had not visited her town, but had changed its name to Foster's Ulcer Gulch. One wonders what Charles Stanton would have thought.

In 1962, Anne Foster leased Ulcer Gulch, still known as Stanton to the locals, to Mr. and Mrs. Al Hayes. The Hayeses refurbished some of the buildings, with the intent of opening the town to the public as a tourist attraction. Mrs. Hayes stated in a 1962 article in the *Arizona Republic* that among other things "there'll be donkey races." After this mention in the newspapers, Stanton once again faded into obscurity.

Chapter 8
Rich Hill Pioneers
Interviews with Clyde Thomason and
Fred Lyman

Clyde Thomason

Clyde Thomason, a long-time resident of Congress, Arizona, probably knows the Rich Hill story as well as anyone alive today, after all he lived it. The soft-spoken eighty-year-old pioneer is one of the few remaining survivors of an era that has long since passed. Clyde was born February 3, 1924, in Wickenburg, Arizona. When he was only ten days old he was taken to live with his family in Octave, a mining town nestled at the foot of Rich Hill, which in its heyday boasted a population of 5,000. They lived on the east side of the mountain in a home made of granite and mud. The floors were dirt, and there was no indoor plumbing, air conditioning, or even electricity. The only source of light was from kerosene lamps. The house is now gone, but remnants of the foundation can still be seen. When I asked Clyde if any rattlesnakes ever got inside he replied, "A few, but not many."

Clyde was a tough little boy with a friendly disposition. He was raised to be honest and had a smile for just about everyone. During his younger years, he attended the Octave School. The tiny schoolhouse served all children up to

Figure 8-1. Clyde Thomason. Photo taken December 14, 2000, outside of his home in Congress, Arizona.

Figure 8-2. Painting of the house Clyde Thomason grew up in.

eighth grade, and only needed nine students to operate. However, because of its size, Clyde was forced to go to nearby Wickenburg for high school. He was a talented musician and could play both the guitar and fiddle. He performed for dances all over Arizona and Nevada with his good friends Fred Lyman (from Octave) and Robert Spurlock (from Burro Creek).

During this time, the towns of Rich Hill, such as Octave and Stanton, were alive and well. Clyde said that Rich Hill was actually a melting pot of races. "There were all types of people: Mexican, Italian, White, Chinese, and Indian." At one time there were at least 3,000 illegal Chinese miners placering along Weaver Creek. As one might expect, there were quite a few disputes (or wars) over the ground. "In those days claims were only ten-foot sections, and they were recorded with a pistol. You needed to have courtesy for other miners if you wanted to stay out of fights. There wasn't much in the way of law enforcement, so each man enforced his own law at the diggings."

I asked Clyde if he could remember anything about the placer operations on Weaver Creek and the amount of gold they were producing. He replied that in the old days most of the miners were finding between twenty and thirty decent sized nuggets a month. There were many attempts to work the boulder-bound gravels of Weaver,

Figure 8-3. Present-day stone ruin believed to have once housed the Weaver Post Office.

but most of these operations failed. However, in 1983–84 there was an operation started near the rock corral just below the Devil's Nest (NE 1/4 of Section 6), which did very well. Sometimes their daily cleanup was 15 ounces or better!

Of all the early Arizona mining towns, Weaver was among the most rowdy and lawless. As it grew in size and prosperity, so did its precarious reputation. It became a hangout for cutthroats and thieves. It was also home to the notorious red-light district. After the 1898 murder of saloon–general store owner William Segna, a newspaper article called for the complete eradication of Weaver because of its unsavory inhabitants. Clyde recalled a saloon built on Weaver Flat near the Myers Mine. "It was a nice place called the Weaver Creek Saloon, the bartender was George Myers." Apparently, Myers had moved to Rich Hill after retiring from his former occupation, a train and bank robber! In fact, a lot of people came to Rich Hill to escape the law. Clyde did not know when the saloon first opened. However, in a photograph given to him by Myers he saw the date 1904 written in the background.

Clyde personally knew the Lucero brothers, Chano and Vincente. These are the same two brothers who gunned down the infamous Charles Stanton after he abused their sister. The Luceros weren't exactly law-abiding citizens, but Clyde spoke fondly of them. He was only a small boy at the time, but he could still remember them vividly.

Figure 8-4. Main Street, Octave, Arizona, with Lion's Peak in the background, circa 1930. (photo courtesy of Sharlot Hall Museum)

He reminisced of the times when the three of them would go searching for gold. It seems that the brothers' eyesight had deteriorated over the years; Clyde on the other hand had excellent vision and was quick to spot the nuggets lying on the ground. He laughed, "I used to reach down, pick up those nuggets and hand them to the Luceros."

He shared with me a story told to him by the eldest brother, Vincente. It seems Chano was fooling around with a married woman and one day the husband caught them in the act. The enraged husband grabbed a knife and attempted to cut Chano's throat. Vincente walked in as the two men were struggling. Scared for his brother's life, Vincente picked up a meat cleaver and in one fatal swing chopped the husband's head clean off his shoulders! The men fled, but Vincente was picked up later by the authorities and sentenced to twenty-one years in the Yuma prison. Clyde doesn't believe Vincente ever served out his sentence.

Clyde spoke of a colorful old fellow named Henry Buck Schoonover, who lived in a tunnel west of Weaver Mountain. Somehow the miner had lost his leg, but this was only a minor setback and didn't keep him from getting around. The crafty oldtimer simply replaced the missing appendage with a stump he carved from a Palo Verde tree. The makeshift leg left him slightly off balance, so he used a 12-gauge shotgun as a cane!

Figure 8-5. Water cart in Octave, Arizona, circa 1920. (photo courtesy of Sharlot Hall Museum)

One evening a young and cocky game warden approached Henry and demanded he show proof of his hunting permit. Henry just leaned back on the porch and shoved his cane in the warden's face and said, "I got your permit, right down the end of these two barrels!" The pale-faced warden took off and was never seen again.

Frank "2-gun" Gillick was another amusing character who lived in a stone house on the east side of Rich Hill. Frank always carried two six-shooters and loved to whip them in and out of their holsters. Clyde began to tell a story about Frank and burst out laughing. It seems that one night he and some other children crept up to the cabin and peeked in through an open window. There was Frank posed in front of a large mirror drawing his pistols. Apparently, he got himself so worked up that he unleashed both barrels, blowing the mirror to pieces!

As a boy, Clyde and the other children would venture up to the Potato Patch to cut down pine trees for Christmas. It seems that on their way down from one of these Christmas tree hunts the children heard a bloodcurdling scream. They scanned the hillsides, but saw nothing. A few minutes later the noise got closer, only this time they saw what was causing the horrible sound. It was a hungry mountain lion not far behind them. The children were terrified and hid under the tree as they slowly made their way down the rocky slope. Clyde said he could see the animal leaping from boulder to

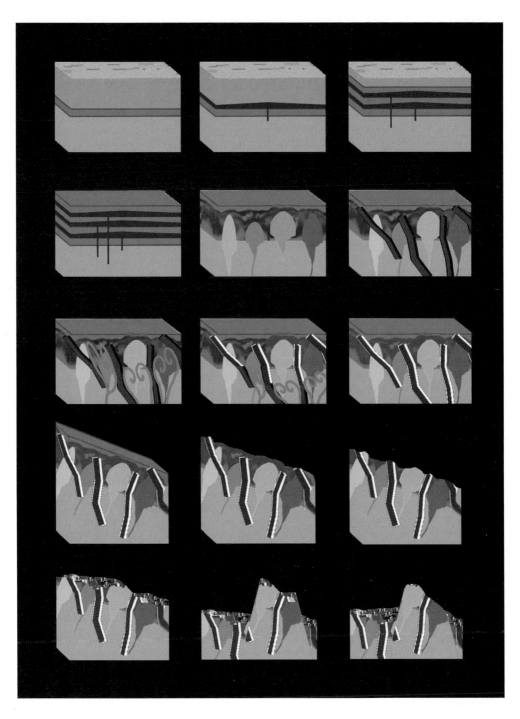

Cartoon diagrams showing the geological evolution of the Rich Hill area, from the beginning (top left) to present (bottom right). For a complete description of these events, see chapter 2.

A satellite image of the greater Rich Hill District and surrounding area. The location of major roads and towns are shown for reference. The box outline shows the area of Rich Hill shown in detail on the next page. Note the large alluvial fan, the center of which is located at the lower left corner of the box outline. The alluvial fan consists of sediment (including gold) washed out of the Rich Hill area by Antelope and Weaver Creeks.

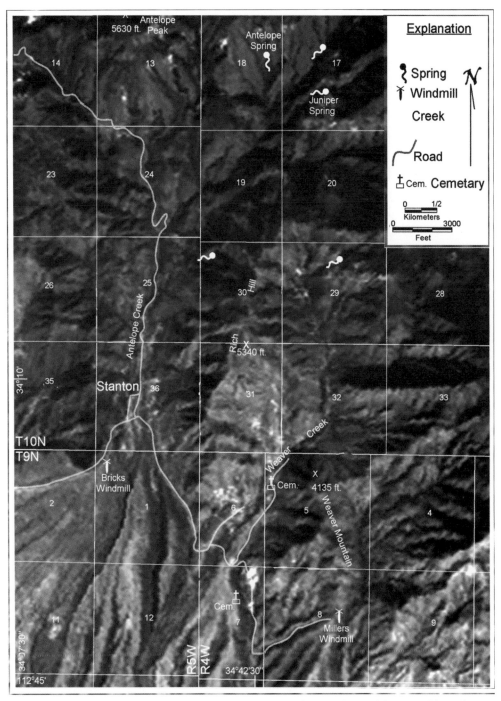

Detailed satellite image of the Rich Hill area. Major roads, landmarks, and the township and range grid with section numbers are shown for reference. The tailings from the Octave Mill (white areas) are clearly visible in the upper right corner of section 7. Many mine dumps can also be seen in sections 6, 31, and 36. The broad flat surface of the upper portion of the alluvial fan extends south and west from where Antelope Creek flows past Stanton.

Weathering along cracks in the Rich Hill Granite has given the distinct "rounded boulder" appearance to this outcrop north of the road between Stanton and Decision Corner. The stone building in the middle left was probably a powder shed for storing explosives in a cool, dry spot at a safe distance from a mine.

The famous "Potato Patch," which yielded many thousands of ounces of gold in the early days of the district. Despite over 140 years of reworking, gold is still found here.

Looking up to Rich Hill and the Potato Patch from the Devil's Nest area. Note the distinctive red color of the soil. This is a classic Red Placer.

Fifteen gold nuggets weighing over 1½ ounces., found in the Devil's Nest area. From left to right: an "L" shaped nugget of ½ ounce, 10 smaller nuggets totaling a little over ½ ounce, and 4 nuggets totaling a little over ½ ounce with the largest weighing 1/3 ounce.

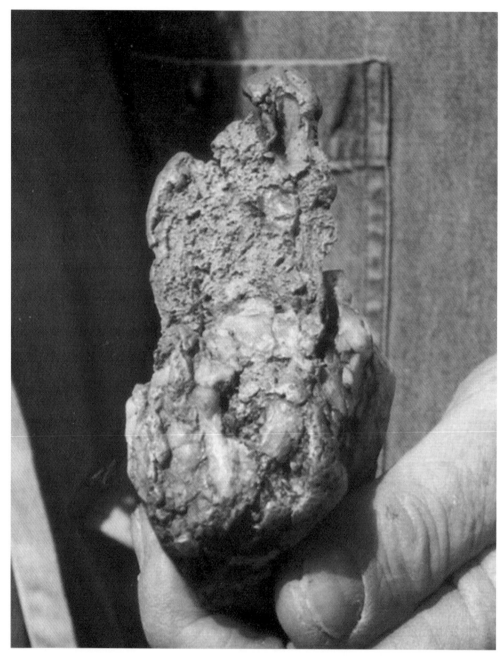

The two-pound "Tongue Nugget," found by Jan and Jess Harkness in March of 2000 with a Minelab SD2200 detector. This quartz and gold specimen, which bears a strong resemblance to specimen gold from below the Octave Mine, was reportedly found on the Lucky Linda claim. Photo courtesy of the Gold Prospector's Association of America.

A 4 ½ ounce nugget from the Devil's Nest area, found at a depth of 1 ½ feet with a Minelab SD2100 detector.

Over 8 ounces of gold nuggets found at various places around the Rich Hill area. The largest nugget, to the right, weighs over 2 ½ ounces.

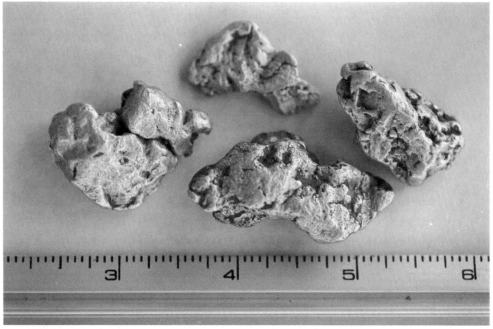

Four large nuggets found in the Rich Hill area with a Minelab SD2100 detector. From the bottom, clockwise: a nugget just under 3 ounces from the Potato Patch, a 2 ½ ounce nugget from the Devil's Nest area, a ½ ounce nugget from the Devil's Nest area, and a 1 1/3 ounce nugget from the Devil's Nest area.

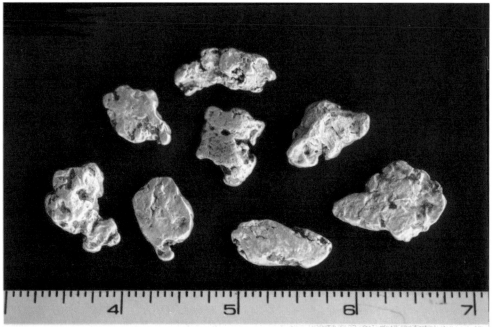

Eight large nuggets between ¼ and ½ ounce found in the Rich Hill area with a Minelab SD2100 detector. From the top nugget, clockwise: nuggets from Weaver Creek, Johnson Mine area, two from the Potato Patch, three from the Devils Nest area, and in the center is a nugget from south of the Octave Mine.

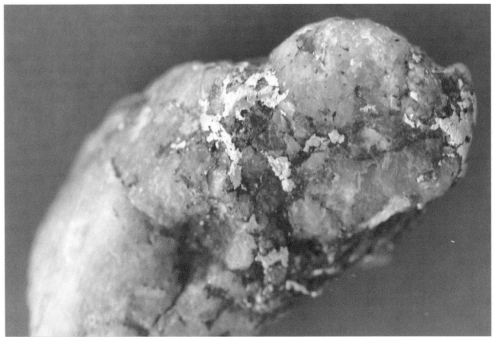

A specimen of quartz and gold from the Devil's Nest area, containing about ½ ounce of gold. The specimen was found with a Minelab SD2100 detector at a depth of a few inches, on a hill below a quartz-gold vein. Specimen is about 4 inches long and 2 inches wide.

A specimen of quartz and gold from the Devil's Nest area, containing about 1/10 ounce of gold. The specimen was found with a Minelab SD2100 detector at a depth of a few inches, on a hill below a quartz-gold vein. Specimen is about 2 inches wide.

Samples of partially oxidized sulfide ore from the Octave Mine. This sample contains galena (silvery metallic) and quartz (white), cut by reddish-brown fracture fillings of hematite. Gold and silver in this ore occur as microscopic particles. The author's fire assay of the whole sample yielded 10 ounces of gold per ton, and 20 ounces of silver per ton. This would have been considered very rich ore, even in the "old days."

Examples of oxidized ore from the Octave Mine. This rock is stained brown and red from the rusting of pyrite to form hematite. White areas are quartz and calcite. Native gold is occasionally found in this type of rock. Fire assay of these samples by the author gave 0.5 ounces of gold per ton and 0.2 ounces of silver per ton.

The old church, one of the few buildings that still remains in Octave.

The Weaver cemetery

The Butterfield Stage Stop, where Charles P. Stanton was gunned down, now serves as Stanton's main office.

The Opera house at Stanton now serves as a bar, dancehall, meeting hall, and a place to conduct weddings.

boulder, getting closer all the while. Amazingly, the lion followed them all the way to the Myers Mine. Clyde was certain they would be attacked at any moment, but luckily they all survived the ordeal without a scratch.

Clyde really doesn't consider himself a true miner, although he has been involved with some aspect of mining his entire life. As a young man he herded goats, placer-mined, and hauled ore at Rich Hill to help support the family. He also dry-washed and rockered to earn extra money to bet—playing billiards in his father's store near Decision Corner. I asked Clyde if he ever found any good-sized nuggets. He held out his hand and curled his fingers into a loop about the size of a walnut, "I found plenty of them like this, but nothing very big."

In his younger years, Clyde used to routinely climb up to the Potato Patch after a good rain to look for gold nuggets lying on the surface. On one such occasion, his brother slipped and tumbled down a rocky bluff. As he fell, he instinctively stuck out his hands in front of him to break the fall. His palms and fingers were bloody from digging down into the soil. He began to cry, but quickly stopped once he realized what his now hurting hands had pushed up out of the loose soil. It was a large gold nugget worth $570! Gold at this time was worth $20.00 per ounce, so the nugget must have weighed approximately 28.5 ounces.

There was a substantial amount of gold being found, but most of the people living at Rich Hill were poor. The depression years were especially tough on families, and the Thomasons were no exception. "There wasn't enough money to buy shoes, so most of us children went barefoot, even during the winter," Clyde said. He remembered times when his calluses got so thick that he could just rake his foot over a jagged rock to get rid of the cactus needles. Other times, he would be running through the rocks and stub a toe, sometimes knocking the nail completely off. To stop the bleeding, he would just stick his foot in the sand or cover it with dirt.

The Great Depression made life difficult for residents of Octave. A few men got jobs with the government work program, which paid $1 a day, however most resorted to placer mining and lived in tents or broken-down shacks. Gold nuggets became the local currency and could be traded for virtually anything. Merchants often used beans as a standard to weigh the gold. Times were so tough that even the animals (horses, goats, burros, etc.) were killed off and sold to make dog food. Clyde said, "Survival was about all you could expect."

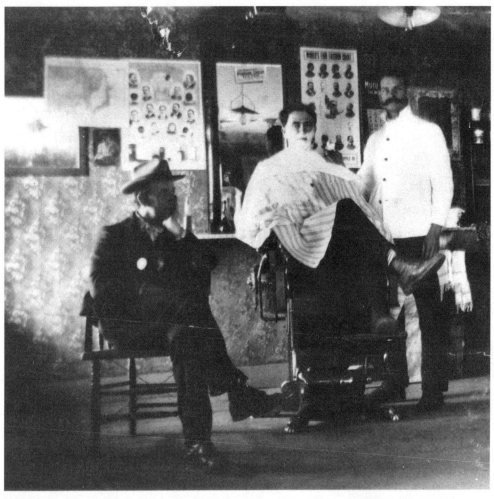

Figure 8-6. Barber shop in the town of Octave, Arizona, circa 1920. (photo courtesy of Sharlot Hall Museum)

At the age of fifteen, Clyde was involved in a tragic accident that would change his life forever. He used to haul ore down from the mines on top of Rich Hill by burro to sell in the town of Wickenburg. The journey down the mountain was long and perilous, so he usually only collected those pieces of rock that appeared to be of high grade. On one of these trips he tried to mount a burro owned by A. V. Moore. This was a big mistake, as the animal bucked wildly, sending poor Clyde whizzing through the air. When he landed his leg twisted and became lodged in a rock crevice, snapping the bone. Clyde was taken to Wickenburg for treatment. The small town doctor, who Clyde believes was drunk at the time, incorrectly set the bone. He complained from the pain, but was forced to wear the cast for over a month. Gangrene inevitably set in and Clyde was shipped off to a hospital in Prescott. He was bed ridden for several months and despite further treatment his leg had to be amputated.

The Thomason family sued the Wickenburg doctor for malpractice, and after a long legal battle eventually won a small settlement. When Clyde turned twenty-one, he used the money to buy the Sunrise Bar and Dance Hall near Congress, Arizona. Customers could enjoy live music, square dancing, and cold beer. There was even roller skating on Wednesday nights, until the wooden floor wore out. He doesn't own the bar anymore, but he does have a polished steel leg as a reminder of that fateful afternoon.

Clyde never worked in the Octave Mine. However, his father and two brothers were employees there, in addition to his uncle who worked as a mule skinner. When the Octave Mine shut down in early 1942, so did most of Rich Hill. The placers were virtually exhausted, and once the area's largest employer closed its doors, there wasn't much reason to stick around. By late 1942, all the homes and water pipes up to ten miles east of Antelope Creek had been removed. The town was totally demolished. Even though Octave barely clung onto existence, the Thomasons continued to stay. The Thomason children moved on, seeking work, and scattered out to return only occasionally. Mr. and Mrs. Thomason lived there at the old rock home until they died. Clyde still maintains the family property.

A few crumbling ruins, tin cans, a portion of the mill, and two graveyards are all that remain of Octave today. Tattered wooden crosses mark the location of numerous gravesites in Weaver Cemetery to the north. Clyde estimates that there are approximately 200 to 300 people buried in Weaver, including some of his own family. He believes most of these deaths were a result of the flu epidemic that swept through the area in 1918.

On December 31, 1946, Clyde married Marie Belle Hastings. They moved to Bishop, California, where Clyde worked at U.S. Vanadium. They lived in Bishop for five years, and then moved to Las Vegas, Nevada, where Clyde was hired at Mercury. This job was the first testing program for the atomic bomb.

Clyde was a member of the Operating Engineers, Local 12 of Southern California and Nevada. Here he maintained generators, which were used in place of commercial power, as the recording equipment was very sensitive to power surges.

Clyde also worked for the prime contractor, Reynolds Electric, at the Nevada test site for twenty-five years as an operator and mechanic. He retired in 1975 to Chloride, Arizona, where he and Marie Belle bought one of the oldest homes in town and remodeled it. Clyde and Marie Belle eventually divorced. He later remarried and is now living in Congress, Arizona, where he operates a karaoke business with his new wife, Jacquie.

Clyde's roots in the mining industry stem back over two generations to when the West was truly wild. His grandfather, Julius Augustus Thomason, told his family that he was born September 29, 1849, in Campbell County, Kentucky. However, the records in Kentucky, and his family, say he was born September 19, 1840. He married Mary E. Right in 1866 and had one son, Julius Francis Thomason. Apparently, Mary and her son died, as there are no records of them.

In 1880, Julius was working in Belleville, Nevada, a town not far from Candelaria. It had two stamp mills, several hotels, seven saloons, and a number of stores and cafes. While living there, Julius married a second time, to Conchetta Flores. They had four children: Lena, Julius Augustus, Jr., George Washington, and Belle Thomason. Clyde's father, George Washington Thomason was born in Candelaria, Nevada, February 22, 1886. By 1880, Candelaria was the largest town in what was then Esmeralda County, Nevada. It boasted ten saloons, two hotels, six stores, three lawyers, and several doctors.

Life in the early frontier mining town was tough. For the first seventeen years, water was hauled in by wagons and sold for a dollar a gallon. There were no sewers, so its citizens were constantly plagued by flies. To make matters worse, the stamp mill, which was a dry crusher, produced an endless cloud of dust. Miners worked ten-hour shifts for $3.50 per day—not much, considering many developed severe lung conditions from the dust. The mining towns thrived for a short while, but after only nine years were virtually abandoned. The Thomasons then moved seven miles up the road to Bodie, California. Here George's father, Julius, taught school and worked as a foreman to one of the mines.

At some point in the 1890s the Thomasons relocated to Octave, Arizona, and Julius once again resumed a career in teaching and mining. Julius worked on and off for the mines and as a schoolteacher in Stanton. He died in Octave, Arizona, on November 30, 1917, and is buried in the Octave cemetery. His little granddaughter, Amilia Thomason, is buried at the head of his grave. Clyde's father, George, worked as a hoist man and blacksmith to the Octave Mine. He placer-mined on Weaver Creek and on occasion worked as a mail carrier. George picked up the mail at the Congress Junction railroad station and delivered it to the Octave mining camp on foot. Sometimes he would receive important cablegrams and would have to run the full distance, nearly eight miles. He spoke Spanish fluently and learned to play the violin while attending high school in Bishop, California. He played it at nearly every dance in Octave and Congress.

One day while placering along Weaver, George met a beautiful young woman named Elvian, who was visiting her mother in Octave. Elvian Sarah Dunham was born July 25, 1888, in Los Angeles, California. When she was two years old the family moved to Jerome, Arizona. There, she went to school until her parents, Matilda and Clarence Dunham, moved to Camp Verde, Arizona.

Matilda's marriage eventually broke down and she and Clarence were divorced. Matilda left on horseback for the Mogollon Rim with Elvian and her brother Clarence. There they built a log cabin complete with a corral. They hunted and trapped game for some time, then moved down to Phoenix. They then left Phoenix for Tucson on bicycles. Shortly after, Elvian went back to Phoenix to work for a doctor, while her mother and brother moved on to Octave.

Elvian's mother, Matilda, was born December 16, 1870, in Boston, Massachusetts. Her grandchildren were never allowed to call her "Grandmother." She always insisted on being called "Bammy." Bammy was the Calamity Jane type of person, and was without a doubt a true pioneer woman. She wore knickerbockers, leather putts, and men's work shirts and shoes.

Once, while bringing her fruit to sell in the company store at the Octave Mine, she was attacked on the trail by a cut-throat Yaqui Indian. He attempted to pull her from her horse, but met with little success. Luckily, Bammy was carrying a brake rod from her wagon, taking it to the mine blacksmith for repair. As he approached, she thrust the brake rod into his belly, knocked him from his horse, and escaped.

She married Pete Angus York (whom Pete Creek is named after) on April 9, 1913. The couple moved to a ranch in Black Water Canyon. Bammy grew an assortment of delicious fruit on the ranch. In fact, her apples won first place at the state fair. She was the owner of the Octave Store and service station and was one of the early real estate developers in Octave. Matilda died April 27, 1939; she is buried in Congress Junction, Arizona.

After meeting, George and Elvian fell in love and were married January 13, 1913. They had six children; Earl, Earnest, Lucille, Clyde, Amelia (who lived only three months), and a baby boy named Willard (who did not live long either).

George worked for the Octave Mine at first, so they had a company house to live in. However, for some reason or other, Elvian decided to build her family their very own home. With her mother's help, she constructed a lovely rock house on the east side of Rich Hill made of granite and mud.

Elvian was an extremely hard worker and was considered one of the better placer miners on Weaver Creek. She was a resourceful woman, and always managed to accomplish any job she set out to do. She cut wood, built roads, mined gold, and built a five-room frame house.

Her husband George became interested in the Rincon Mine, and eventually leased the property in 1937–1938 from a gentleman by the name of Greer (records list a Mr. Spear as the operator). The Thomasons lived on the property for a short while. According to Clyde, "The ore was not exceptionally rich, but it was good enough to cover expenses." George later opened up a mercantile/grocery store and pool hall near Octave.

Their children eventually moved away, but the couple remained at Rich Hill for many years. They were liked by everyone and regarded as honest folks. Sadly, George W. Thomason ended his own life in 1962.

The eldest son, Earl Thomason, was born September 16, 1913, in Wickenburg. However, he spent much of his young life in the town of Octave. Times were tough, and Earl, being the oldest, was forced to share the burden of supporting the family. Despite being very young, Earl was a large boy and quite strong for his age. He worked alongside his father placer-mining on Weaver Creek. He was put to work in the Octave Mine when he was just fourteen years old. Later, around 1933 or 1934, a mining company leased his father's claims and Earl was hired as the shovel operator. In 1937, he was hired as the clean-up man for the Lynx Creek Dredging Company, out of Prescott, Arizona. Earl told Clyde that they were getting close to a troy pound (12 ounces) of gold per day.

In 1941, he was called into the army and placed in the construction battalion. After leaving the army, Earl worked in construction as a cat and can man. He then moved farther west to Las Vegas, and made excellent money working at the Nevada test site. During this time Earl had become very overweight and his health suffered. He was told repeatedly by the company doctor to lose weight or he would have to be laid off. He did manage to lose some, but couldn't seem to keep it off. Earl had a heart attack in 1971. He died at age fifty-seven and is buried in Congress, Arizona.

Earnest Thomason was born August 28, 1917, in Wickenburg, Arizona. Like his older brother, Earnest was a hard worker and a good miner. As a boy, he placer-mined at Rich Hill to help feed the family and earn extra spending cash. During the depression, he was told by his father George that he had to earn at least 65¢ for butter before he could spend money on anything else. A difficult task, as gold was only worth $20.00 per ounce.

Earnest, or Ernie, also began working in the hard rock mines at an early age. He ran a jackhammer up in the stopes of the Octave Mine. The working conditions during this time would have been extremely poor. Life underground was dark, dusty, noisy, not to mention dangerous. Cave-ins were always a concern, but there was another less conspicuous threat lurking about. As the miner's drill bits and other mechanized equipment bored into the auriferous veins, they released millions of microscopic par-ticles, causing the air to become laden with heavy clouds of quartz dust. Breathing this air for any length of time causes the lungs to slowly harden, a condition known as silicosis. Proper respirators were either not available or too expensive, so Ernie, like many others, developed miner's "consumption" or "rock in the box," a condition that would plague him for the rest of his life.

Ernie led a tough life. At the Octave mining camp, he was nicknamed "Wild Hair" for his crazy driving habits. Ernie would go tearing along the dirt roads and managed to get the old truck sideways on virtually every curve. Once he picked up some men who were walking to the mine to rustle work. After Ernie hit the first curve the men demanded to get out, saying they would rather walk than ride with him. Ernie had a quick temper and was not known to back down from a fight. On one occasion, while arguing with his older brother, Ernie kept him out of the house for several days with a .22 rifle. Every time Earl would poke his head up from behind the rocks, Ernie would take a shot at him.

During the war, Ernie and Clyde set off to California to find work. In Bakersfield, they got jobs driving a truck down in the pit under the shovel for the Union Rock Company. They quickly grew tired of the job and departed for Los Angeles. The brothers then got work with the union hall, which hired men to do piecework by the day or by the hour, such as off-loading boats, boxcars, or trucks. After several weeks they decided to go farther north to San Francisco and finally Spokane, Washington. They worked doing odd jobs, but eventually returned to Arizona. Ernie died while still a young man, at the age of forty-six, from heart trouble. He is buried in Congress, Arizona.

Lucille Thomason was born in Prescott, Arizona, on July 29, 1921. Lucille was the only girl in a family of three boys, so she had to learn to be tough in order to survive. She was physically stronger than most of the boys who were a few years older than she was. Once she beat up a gang of boys after they had given her little brother Clyde a bloody nose. She went to school at the Octave School. Many winters she was sent to school barefoot, as the family made very little money placer mining.

Lucille was considered a pretty little girl with naturally curly hair. She attracted the attention of a California man from Eastman Kodak Company, who had come to visit the mine. He took her picture standing on a big rock, picking fruit from a prickly pear cactus. The picture took first place in a contest sponsored by Kodak.

Fred Lyman

Fred Lyman was born January 2, 1923, in Prescott, Arizona. Fred spent much of his young life in the town of Octave, Arizona. He began attending the Octave School in 1927, at the age of four. He did not stay long, as his mother got into an

Figure 8-7. Fred Lyman. Photo taken January 30, 2001, near Congress, Arizona.

argument with someone from the school and pulled him out. This was a problem because the tiny school needed at least nine students to operate, and Fred was the ninth.

Fred is a talented musician and has mastered the guitar and fiddle, both of which he taught himself how to play. He won the Arizona state championship several times in the early 1950s for his fiddle playing. Fred and Clyde Thomason met when they were only a few years old, and have been lifelong friends. Together they performed for the Saturday night dances held at Octave and Congress. Unfortunately, Fred has suffered several mild strokes and no longer plays music.

Fred worked for a short time at the Octave Mine mucking ore, a job that paid $4.00 per day. I asked Fred what it was like working in the mines. "Life underground was miserable, so I quit," he replied. "Clyde and I did a little placer mining to earn some extra money to buy .22 shells and play pool in his dad's store," Fred said. Mining never really sparked an interest in Fred. He found ranching, on the other hand, very appealing. He worked for Jim Ranking breaking horses and tending cattle. He also competed in many rodeos; his specialty was bull riding.

Fred knew the Lucero brothers, Chano and Vincente. He said, "They were a rough pair, and not too many people messed with them. They were the type of guys who would kill someone just for the fun of it." He spoke of another unusual fellow named Floyd Price, who lived in a cabin on top of Rich Hill. Floyd was a World War I disabled veteran, who, according to Fred and Clyde, was a little crazy in the head. "You always had to be careful when approaching Floyd, because he was quick to pull a shotgun on people he didn't recognize," they said. He worked day after day placering the gravels of Potato Patch, apparently with good success.

Fred said, "Floyd found a lot of gold, but he always shared it with us kids." He would sit Clyde and his sister Lucille down on his lap, reach into his pocket, and pull out a fistful of nuggets for them. Fred recalled a time when Floyd got so drunk that he tossed a handful of nuggets onto the bar room floor and yelled, "Leave those alone, they're for the birds!" Then one night some Mexicans from Phoenix got him drunk and stole all his gold; shortly afterward his lifeless body was found near the creek. Floyd's murderer(s) were never apprehended.

Unlike Floyd, Manuel Lieus was not kind hearted. Fred and Clyde used to temporarily "borrow" burros from his corral to ride. Apparently this didn't sit well with Manuel and he routinely took shots at them. Manuel was not the nicest guy in the world, to say the least. He would hire people to tend his goats, and then when they asked for payment he would kill them. Clyde said, "One poor guy worked for two years without wages. When he asked for his money Manuel murdered him, hid the body in a patch of cactus, and piled stones on top of him." The local judge was called out to investigate, but came to the conclusion that the man died of natural causes—typical Rich Hill justice! He even killed a prospector by hitting him in the back of the head with a crowbar, and then stole his gold. Fred and Clyde could think of at least five people that Manuel had murdered.

Fred's father worked as the Octave Mine superintendent from 1924 to 1928. He was also the postmaster, local veterinarian, and deputy sheriff. On a hunch, he pegged some ground northeast of the Octave and named it the Lyman Mine. However, the ore was not of exceptional quality and the mine never sold, as the asking price was quite large. Then in 1940 the Octave Mine was forced to lease the property because it wanted to tunnel beneath it. The first payment the Lymans received was $10,000, a considerable amount of money at the time. The Lyman Mine was never really developed, instead just enough work was done for the annual assessment. Fred said, "Our family was lucky, we always had enough money to eat and buy clothes."

Fred's parents left Octave in 1928 for Prescott, and then went on to Flagstaff. His father was always drawn to the Octave area and returned for a short while, until his wife finally persuaded him to move down to Phoenix. Fred left Octave permanently at the age of eighteen. Fred eventually returned to the area and now lives a few minutes away from Clyde in Congress.

Chapter 9
Full Circle: Gold, Guns, and God in the 1970s

The more things change in the Weaver District the more they remain the same. Over the years many have been lured by the promise of easy money, power, and the hope of a better life. Some prospered, others failed, most go unremembered. A few, like Charles Stanton, made a mark on history. Stanton was a self-proclaimed man of God, and on first inspection an upstanding citizen. Yet behind his charming façade lay the heart of a murderer and thief. Stanton was a man who schemed, planned, and plotted to arrange events to his advantage. Ultimately, Stanton's own actions caused his downfall. Stanton's story is not unique. Here is the story of another self-proclaimed man of God who came to Rich Hill to seek his fortune. His Rich Hill adventure starts with a classic gold mine swindle and ends with the expected, a robbery of Wells Fargo.

The Swindle

In 1975, a group of men founded a company whose purported goal was to reprocess the tailings piles of the Octave gold mine, which had lain dormant for over thirty years. The Rhenium Corporation of Clearwater, Florida, was incorporated on April 9, 1975. Corporate officers were identified as William F. Muller—president; Bruce G. Allen—vice president; Wallace E. Chaney—vice president; and M. A. Fernandez—secretary/treasurer. William F. Muller and M. A. Fernandez, along with Clinton M. T. Green were appointed directors. Corporate documents claim that the company purchased the Octave and the 16-to-1 mines, the equipment on both mines, and the Octave mine dumps on April 10, 1975, for a price of $617,274.93. It was the intent of the Rhenium Corporation to mine the Octave and 16-to-1 mines and reprocess the tailings of the Octave. In order to place the mines in production and to acquire sufficient operating funds until income from production was available, corporate management intended either to merge with a publicly traded company or to file a stock offering to sell $100,000 worth of stock at $1.00 per share. These intentions were made known to investors in an April 28, 1976, letter to stockholders from William F. Muller.

Included in the April 28, 1976, package to stockholders was an evaluation of the geology of the Rich Hill area and the Octave ore by Bruce G. Allen, a chemical engineer formerly engaged in catalytic converter research (which involves the use of platinum metal) at Argonne National Laboratory. This evaluation was presented in a report to the Rhenium Corporation dated March 14, 1975. In the evaluation, Allen claimed that average Octave ore contains, in addition to native gold, chemical compounds such as gold chloride and platinum chloride. Allen also claimed that the Octave ore contained recoverable amounts of platinum, palladium, rhenium, iridium, gallium, and rare earth elements. The ore grade was listed at ½ ounce of gold, 1 ounce of palladium, ½ ounce of platinum, and 1 ounce of rhenium per ton of material. Allen claimed that these metals would not have been recovered by the "gravitational gold recovery" methods used in the past at the Octave gold mine. However, he claimed that they could be recovered using an acid-leaching method, which involved submersing the ore in a pool of concentrated hydrochloric and nitric acids, followed by treatment with chemicals to precipitate the metals or salts. It was estimated that it would take approximately six years to process 500,000 tons of material. The stockholder package of April 28, 1976, claimed that "even at the present low prices for the aforesaid metals, each share of Rhenium Corporation will earn over $15.00 per share before corporate taxes over the next six years according to Mr. Allen's evaluation."

This evaluation must have sounded quite impressive to potential stockholders, as it is filled with scientific jargon and geologic terms, most of which have no relevance whatsoever to Rich Hill. Using their stockholder package, the Rhenium Corporation managed to sell $100,000 of stock to an unsuspecting, though not entirely innocent, group. In the summer of 1976, the Reverend Jack M. Oliphant, the executive director of the Ranch Challenge Hallelujah People acquired 200,000 shares of the Rhenium Corporation at 50¢ per share. These shares were then offered to members of the Ranch Challenge congregation in 1000-share lots. The stock came secured with a guarantee that if the shares were unsatisfactory in one year's time, the church would buy them back at a price of 55¢ each. The guarantee was secured by the Hallelujah Fruit Company, a subsidiary of the Ranch Challenge Hallelujah People, Inc. and the 1500 acres of land that they owned in Pasco County, Florida. The Rhenium Corporation seemed like a reasonable investment opportunity to support the workings of a religious group and all appeared to be on the level.

The Wild West Returns

Figure 9-1. Reverend Jack M. Oliphant. Photo by Mike Smith. (courtesy of Phoenix Newspapers Inc.)

In the winter of 1976 Reverend Jack Oliphant, known to his followers as the Preacherman, had a vision in which "the Lord told him to come to [the Octave mine]" in Arizona. The Preacherman gathered together about fifty of his followers, who were known as the Hallelujah Boys, piled them into a motley collection of old buses, trucks, and cars, and relocated to Arizona. The Hallelujah boys were a group of self-described misfits rescued from drugs, defeatism, and crime. They arrived at the Octave Mine sometime between December 1976 and January 1977. The group took up residence in some of the abondoned buildings and started placer-mining operations in the wash beds below the mine, believing that their purchase of the Rhenium Corporation stock gave them ownership of the Octave gold mine and surrounding land.

"Preacher" Jack Oliphant had grand dreams for both his followers and the old ghost town of Octave. "We're just eating jackrabbits and rice right now. We haven't got much except religion. But when you got Jesus Christ everything is different. We'll have a Hallelujah House here soon, maybe a town later. We'll build a lake here in the desert with fish in it. Why we've even got apple trees and a vineyard planted." Oliphant and his Hallelujah Boys started hauling water to their placer mine and began extracting gold using their young muscle and a Rube-Goldberg gold sluice. The Preacherman viewed this operation as a potential Utopia and felt he was giving the young kids an alternative to the life they had on the streets. In his own words, he felt he had taken "the garbage of the land" and given them "work, self-respect, and a sense of family."

Clyde Thomason knew Preacher Jack Oliphant quite well. Clyde said Oliphant passed himself off to everyone as a God-fearing man, and most people bought it. They thought it was wonderful that he had made his mission to help get troubled kids back on track, and give them hope, work, and a place to live. Oliphant claimed that he and

Figure 9-2. The Hallelujah Boys' sluice. Photo by Mike Smith. (courtesy of Phoenix Newspapers Inc.)

128

his "children" were going to work the Octave, but the Preacher was no more a hard rock miner than Charles Stanton was a humanitarian. Oliphant used his religous image to his advantage, especially when it came to charitiable donations. Whenever he needed something he would drive into Prescott and pay the local businesses a visit. Clyde didn't know all the things that were donated to Oliphant, but he did remember the Preacher talked someone out of a vehicle by saying it was for the "children."

Clyde recalled that many of the "children" received disability checks from the state due to various mental conditions. Oliphant, acting on their behalf, collected these checks. It was rumored that most of the money found its way into the Preacher's pocket. Clyde said, "Oliphant was supposed to be helping them kids, but I think they were helping him more than anything."

Oliphant's Utopia may have sounded good to some, but it didn't sit too well with Carl O. Carlson and his trio of armed guards. Carlson and his wife lived in a group of trailers directly across the road from the old Octave buildings. Carlson also claimed to own the Octave Mine in partnership with the CMC Corporation. Unfortunately for Carlson, the Hallelujah Boys

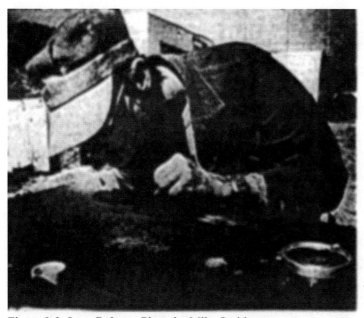

Figure 9-3. Jesse Roberts. Photo by Mike Smith. (courtesy of Phoenix Newspapers Inc.)

chose a campsite less than 500 yards away. With the two groups living in close proximity and contesting ownership of the mine, tensions quickly began to run high. Carlson hired Steve Fosnot, Fosnot's son David, and Rocko Simmons as armed guards to protect the property and mining claims.

The Hallelujah Boys were also armed. Oliphant began to work the placer operations with a loaded .38 revolver on his hip and Al Haynes, a miner working with the Hallelujah Boys, was armed with a .45-caliber automatic pistol. The sheriff's department was called out to investigate several incidents in January and February of 1977. The Carlson group charged that shots had been fired at their radio antennas and that someone tried to steal the auto batteries that they used to power their electric lights. In response, Steve Fosnot grabbed his .357, fired a few shots into the air, and the intruder "took off like a jackrabbit." Rocko Simmons, who the Hallelujah Boys referred to as the "big, fat, frog," claimed that the religious group kept a lookout on a nearby hill armed with a .30-.30 rifle and a CB radio.

The Hallelujah Boys responded to these charges by claiming that their camp had been shot at on several occasions. In one case, a shot aimed at their dog narrowly missed Jesse Roberts's six-month old baby. The Preacherman also charged that he had been pistol-whipped alongside his head by the Carlson group when he confronted them about shootings. After that, someone fired six shots into a parked car that belonged to a visitor of the Hallelujah Boys' camp. Throughout the confrontation, Oliphant believed that he owned the Octave Mine and surrounding lands and that litigation would finally settle the case. Once ownership of the area was established, Preacher

Figure 9-4. Jack Oliphant at Octave, February 1977. Photo by Mike Smith. (courtesy of Phoenix Newspapers Inc.)

Jack felt his Utopia would come to fruition. Jesse Roberts, on the other hand, was much more pragmatic about the situation. "It seems the law of the land in this part of Arizona still basically depends on who has the gun," he said.

Clyde Thomason confirmed the tension between the Hallelujah Boys and the Carlson group. Clyde personally witnessed one of the near shoot-outs between the two rivals. Carlson (or someone in his employ) blockaded the main road out of Octave, so Oliphant was forced to drive his pickup down the rough road below the dump. When he came around the bend Carlson's group drew their guns. Oliphant started to yell and some of the Hallelujah Boys came running with their guns drawn. Clyde said, "There was people hiding behind cactus, boulders, and anything else they could find!" Oliphant spotted Clyde and yelled, "Thomason, you're going to be my witness. You've seen what they've done here." Clyde said he was more interested in getting the heck out of there than in being a witness.

Tensions continued to run high during the winter of 1978, culminating with the accidental shooting of Preacher Jack Oliphant. On March 20, Oliphant's car stalled on a dirt barricade that had been erected on the access road to the Octave Mine by Carlson and his guards. Oliphant said that when he stepped out of his vehicle he found himself covered by weapons drawn by Carlson's three guards. Oliphant reached into his vehicle and removed a 16-gauge shotgun to defend himself. As he pulled the weapon barrel first from the vehicle, the shotgun discharged, striking Oliphant in the right el-

130

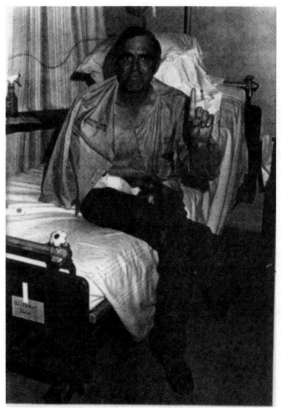

Figure 9-5. Jack Oliphant in a Phoenix hospital shortly after the shooting. (photo courtesy of Phoenix Newspapers Inc.)

bow. The injury resulted in Preacher Jack losing most of his right arm. Incidentally, the mound of dirt erected by Carlson and his men still stands as a barricade at the entrance to the Octave Mine and can only be traversed by vehicles with high ground clearance.

Based on the shooting and other incidents where weapons were brandished in a threatening manner, the Yavapai County Sheriff's Office charged Oliphant with exhibiting a deadly weapon. The charge was filed while he was recovering from his injury in a Phoenix hospital. At his initial court appearance, Oliphant stated that he did not want a court-appointed attorney but would "use the Lord" and represent himself "through prayer." Superior Court Judge James Hancock appointed John Stallings to assist Oliphant in his defense. The Yavapai County Attorney's Office asked for a dismissal of the case, citing insufficient evidence for a conviction. In a strange twist, Oliphant opposed both the dismissal of charges or any plea bargain, stating that he wanted to give testimony regarding the troubles at Octave. He said that he had been trying for months to bring charges involving the other incidents at Octave and wanted to use the court as a public forum "to clear the air and get the facts made public."

The rightful ownership of the Octave Mine and surrounding placer claims would need to be determined in a civil court. However, it is unlikely that Preacher Jack Oliphant and the Hallelujah Boys ever had a legitimate claim to the Octave Mine. Instead, they found themselves on the receiving end of a stock swindle. The case was brought to the attention of public officials when Jack Oliphant was pulled over during a routine traffic stop in Mohave County on September 8, 1976. For some reason Oliphant presented a copy of the Rhenium Corporation investment portfolio to the sheriff who had stopped him. The documents were forwarded to the Securities Division of the Arizona Corporation Commission that same day. Arizona officials then contacted the Office of the Comptroller in the State of Florida regarding the Rhenium Corporation and the Octave gold mine. In the spring of 1977, the State of Florida's Division of Securities launched an investigation into the dealings of the Rhenium Corporation. A subsequent review of Bruce Allen's "Report and Evaluation of Octave Mine Ore" by the State of Arizona's Bureau of Geology and Mineral Technology found the report to be "without reasonable scientific basis." In March of 1980, Wallace Eugene Chaney (vice president of the Rhenium Corporation) was arrested in Las Vegas, Nevada, when Yavapai County special in-

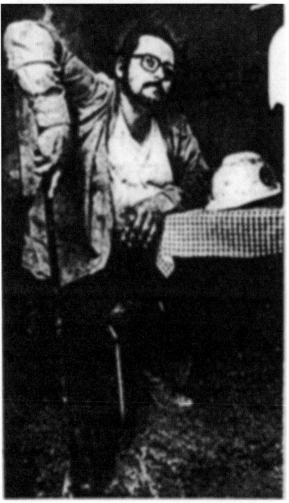

Figure 9-6. Rocko Simmons, one of Carlson's guards. Photo by Mike Smith. (courtesy of Phoenix Newspapers Inc.)

vestigators followed Chaney's Japanese wife from Phoenix to Las Vegas. In addition to working in a Phoenix massage parlor, Mrs. Chaney operated a combination health clinic and massage parlor for women and taught the "Oriental art of massage." She ended up leading investigators directly to Chaney's apartment. Chaney was charged with at least thirteen felony counts of fraud for allegedly selling worthless stock in several Arizona corporations whose assets listed interests in several played-out gold mines including the Octave and the 16-to-1. The investigation in Arizona involved both investment fraud and salting of gold mines. In addition, Chaney had been indicted in Alabama on fraud charges and for failing to appear at his arraignment hearing, had

Figure 9-7. Steve Fosnot, left, and his son, David. Both were hired as guards by C.O. Carlson. Photo by Mike Smith. (courtesy of Phoenix Newspapers Inc.)

a warrant issued for his arrest in Florida on charges of unlawful flight to avoid prosecution, and had been arrested in Japan for allegedly operating a currency black market scheme.

The feud between Oliphant's Hallelujah boys and Carlson's armed guards wasn't the only incident in the Rich Hill area during this time period. Between 1976 and 1979 the Yavapai County Sheriff's Office answered more than 100 calls in response to potential violence. The main problem, according to Yavapai County deputy sheriff, Jody Larue, was that "Lord alone knows who owns what claim." Larue said that most incidents were harmless and usually involved only a couple of guys waving their arms at each other and exchanging obscenities, but that in some cases tensions were high enough for the feuds to erupt into shootouts. An anonymous bearded prospector summarized a particular situation by saying: "There's one trigger happy SOB out there chasing folks off'n their own claims. He's gonna get hisself shot fulla holes one of these days. May just hafta do it meself."

By the 1980s, when gold hit $800 an ounce, things got so crazy that the police and propane refueling trucks refused to come out to Octave. Clyde Thomason recalled one guy that mounted a machine gun on the back of his backhoe to protect himself while he was mining.

It was during the late 1970's that members of the Lost Dutchman's Mining Association (LDMA) began to routinely visit the area and the town of Stanton experienced something of a reincarnation. LDMA members began to park along Antelope Creek and pan for gold. They also would camp among the historical ruins of the town of Stanton. In a bit of historical irony, Stanton, long tainted by its bloody history, became known as the place where the friendly, outgoing, solid citizens would hang out. The members of the LDMA were not looking to get rich and instead considered themselves recreational prospectors. They were drawn to Stanton as much for the beauty and solitude of the area as for the rich gold deposits. The group purchased the town and mineral rights to some of the surrounding areas in 1978.

Probably the most colorful resident of Stanton during this time period was Roy Caswell, a seventy-year-old retired well digger who wore a pacemaker and could "climb the hills with a five-year-old kid until the kid dropped from exhaustion." Caswell acted as the caretaker of Stanton, greeting drop-ins and prospective members and telling colorful stories about the history of the area. Caswell was a self-styled dowser and witcher who used a forked wooden stick to mark the spot where the camp's well was to be dug. He also used metal wires to witch the site of what he believed was a "glory-hole." According to the last reports from the area, Roy had dug a shaft over thirty feet deep using nothing but a shovel, a hand-cranked windlass, a bucket, and the sweat of his brow. He was convinced that he was a mere ten feet away from a "pretty good gold deposit." If he found it, it never made it into the history books.

If You Can't Find Gold, There's Always Wells Fargo

Jack Oliphant's Arizona story did not end with his involvement in the Rhenium Corporation and the controversy over ownership of the Octave gold mine. Sometime between 1978 and 1982, Oliphant and some members of his band left the Rich Hill area, moved north to a remote ranch outside of Kingman, Arizona, and joined with a group known as the "Arizona Patriots." The conditions at the ranch were reportedly quite primitive, lacking both electricity and plumbing. They did have one little Honda generator, which they used to sit up all night and watch the movie *Red Dawn* three or four times in a row. In 1982 the group began a campaign of filing frivolous lawsuits, designed to clog the Arizona court system. Lawsuits were filed by members who claimed that they did not need auto registrations or licenses to drive on highways. The suits were filed against anyone who acted against a Patriot and included sheriff's deputies, highway patrolmen, jailers, judges, and tow truck operators.

In 1983 and 1984, the group published a monthly journal, *The Arizona Patriot*, that printed diatribes against government officials, calls for "Christian Patriots" to band together, and reprints of articles from a variety of anti-Semitic and conspiracy-oriented political publications. In June 1984 the Arizona Patriots issued a collective indictment against all elected Arizona officials and threatened to conduct a grand jury inquest unless those officials resigned within thirty days. The group stated that failure to comply with this indictment would result in the death penalty being imposed upon conviction.

The group drew the attention of the FBI in 1984 when its members began to openly espouse desires to overthrow the United States government, destroy certain government facilities, and kill those in opposition to their desires. Among their intended targets were Arizona Governor Bruce Babbitt, U.S. District Judge Paul Rosenblatt, and officers of the state Department of Public Safety. An undercover agent who was able to infiltrate the group recorded their conversations for the next two years.

In January of 1986 the group began to develop a plot to finance their large-scale ambitions. According to an FBI affidavit, they planned to rob a Wells Fargo Armored Service Corporation armored car as it carried money from a Laughlin, Nevada, casino into Arizona on U.S. Highway 93. The plan was to fire a rocket made of potassium chlorate, dynamite, and axle grease into the cab of the truck and kill the two guards. The vehicle would then be loaded into an eighteen-wheel trailer and driven to a remote desert site. The money was going to be laundered through a Las Vegas casino and used to finance the establishment of a white-supremacist firearms- and survival-training compound.

Before the robbery could take place, Oliphant and seven other men were arrested on charges of conspiracy to commit bank fraud, possession and manufacture of illegal weapons, and assaulting a federal officer. After the arrests federal agents raided a Patriot camp and confiscated plans for building bombs, large quantities of illegal weapons, explosive materials, a homemade blowgun, night-vision goggles, pamphlets depicting nuclear war, gas masks, spent shell casings, numerous rocket ammunition crates, and publications of the *Aryan Nations*. The federal grand jury indictment stated that the group planned a terrorism campaign directed toward the U.S. government and Jews, including bomb attacks against a synagogue, the federal building in Phoenix, the Ogden, Utah, Internal Revenue Service facility, abortion clinics, and the Simon Weisenthal Center in Los Angeles.

Of those arrested, three men, including Jack Oliphant, were sentenced to four-year prison terms, three were given five years probation, one was released, and one escaped from custody. In prison, Oliphant wrote a seventy-page manuscript titled *To Alter or Abolish the Government*. In this document, Oliphant states that an "all-out, do or die, to the last man civil war" is the only way patriots can "throw off one status of citizenship while retaining the territory in which they reside."

After being released from prison in 1989, Oliphant and his wife retired to their Hephzibah Ranch forty miles southeast of Kingman. Still, Oliphant was not through with controversy. In 1995, shortly before his death, Oliphant was questioned about his connection to Timothy McVeigh. Oliphant and McVeigh both had mailboxes at the same Kingman, Arizona, mailroom. Oliphant denied any connection with McVeigh or the Oklahoma City bombing and no charges were filed against him. Oliphant died at the age of seventy-one in Kingman, Arizona.

Chapter 10

Metal Detector History, Evolution, and Contribution to the Rich Hill Rushes (1978–Modern Day)

Of all the placer gold deposits in the Southwest, probably none is more intriguing to electronic prospectors than Rich Hill. This rocky, granite-strewn mountain is credited as being the single richest placer gold deposit in the state. While there is no doubt many of Arizona's other gold districts have produced tremendous quantities of gold, none has rewarded modern-day detectorists with more large nuggets than the infamous Rich Hill. It is difficult to estimate the total number of ounces that have been recovered with metal detectors, as most discoveries are never reported. However, considering detectors have been in use on Rich Hill for nearly thirty years, an estimate of several thousand ounces seems completely reasonable. In the following chapter we will explore the development of metal detector technology, and how that technology has been put to use at Rich Hill.

The Invention and Development of the Metal Detector

It is believed that Professor Alexander Graham Bell, the inventor of the telephone, was among the first to experiment with electrical induction devices for locating metals. On July 2 1881, Charles Guiteau shot President James A. Garfield twice with a heavy caliber pistol. One of the bullets grazed his arm while the other lodged somewhere within his back. He was immediately rushed to a doctor, but because medical science during this time was rather crude very little could be done to help him. The x-ray machine had not yet been invented so the physicians had no real way of determining the location of the bullet that was still imbedded within his body. After thirty days the position of the bullet was still not known and the president's condition continued to deteriorate. Garfield's doctors turned to Professor Bell for help, asking him to bring

137

his "metal finding" invention to the White House. A description of this device is given in a book titled *The Life and Work of James A. Garfield*, written in 1881 by John Clark Ridpath:

> The induced electrical current, and the interference there-with by the presence of a metallic body, were the fundamental facts of the invention. The instrument consisted of two circular primary coils of insulated copper three inches in diameter and half an inch in thickness, the one being constructed of No. 19 wire, and containing between seven and eight ohms of resistance, forming the primary coil, and the other of No. 28 or 30 wire, giving more than eighty ohms of resistance, forming the secondary coil, the two being connected in separate metallic circuits. In the circuit with the former there was placed an electrical battery and a spring vibrator, the latter so adjusted as to make a very rapid series of "breaks" of circuit, sending a hundred or more electrical pulsations over the circuit and around the primary coil of wire per second. A hand telephone was placed in the circuit with the secondary coil. The batteries being connected, and the vibrator set in motion, the secondary coil was placed so as to cover the primary and the operator having the telephone at his ear, hears the pulsations of the primary current sent through the vibrator with each motion of its spring, an induced current being produced in the secondary coil by its contiguity with the primary.

When tested in the air it was discovered that the machine could detect a normal-shaped bullet at a distance of 2½ inches, and up to five inches when the bullet was flattened out. However, when actually put to the test on the president, the results were inconclusive. James A. Garfield died September 19, 1881, making him the second president of the United States to be assassinated.

While Alexander Graham Bell may have been the first to experiment with metal detection devices, it is Dr. Gerhard R. Fisher who is credited as being the father of the metal detector.

During the 1920s, Dr. Fisher was working as a research engineer in Los Angeles, California. His work on aircraft radio detection finders attracted not only the attention of other scientists, but the military as well. In the 1930s Fisher was hired by the U.S. Navy to install a radio detection finder aboard one of their dirigibles, the USS *Macon*. It was aboard this "floating ship" that Fisher noticed that some form of external interference was canceling out the direction-finding abilities of his instruments. He determined that the source of this interference was somehow linked to the large metal buildings and mineralized mountain chains beneath the ship.

Figure 10-1. Jim Straight with an M-Scope metal detector.

Building upon this discovery Fisher founded Fisher Research Laboratory in 1931, in a garage behind his home in Palo Alto, California. With the help of four employees he began producing the very first patented metal detector, the "Metallascope." In comparison to today's modern metal detectors the M-Scope was a monstrous device consisting of two large, flat wooden boxes containing simple copper coils, five vacuum tubes, and a few assorted components. Despite its less than "user friendly" size, the M-Scope soon became the accepted standard in metal detection equipment across the world.

The first common mass-produced detectors were the very basic beat frequency oscillator (BFO) type used during World War II to locate buried anti-personnel and tank mines. These early detectors were nothing short of clumsy giants. They required large heavy batteries and often a wooden wheelbarrow to cart them around in. Besides being heavy and cumbersome, they were only able to detect targets the size of a baseball. The transistorized BFOs of the 1950s were lighter and more compact than the earlier vacuum tube types, but were still not well suited for prospecting. Despite their limitations, they did prove useful on the battlefields and provided the necessary framework for more advanced circuitry.

Transmit-receive or (TR) machines were developed during the same time period as the BFOs. They became very popular in the 1960s for coin and treasure hunting. They achieved better detection depth, but still had difficulty handling ground mineralization. Consequently, electronic prospecting, or "nugget shooting" really didn't gain momentum until the invention of the lightweight, ground-canceling very low frequency (VLF) detectors.

The first VLF metal detectors were developed in the 1970s, and operated in the 3–30 kHz range. This new breed of detectors (especially those operating at the lowest end of the spectrum) was able to locate metallic objects buried even deeper than its predecessors could. It was also discovered that a large percentage of the iron mineralization that plagued the earlier BFO and TR detectors could be eliminated or balanced out using these lower frequencies. The ability to cope with "hot ground" was a tremendous breakthrough. For the first time in history, electronic prospectors had an effective tool for working the highly conductive soils typical of goldfields. The invention of the VLF detector provided a much-needed boost to the still-struggling hobby. VLF technology continued to change and improve over the years. However, it was the pulse induction (PI) metal detectors that were to cause the biggest stir in the gold-prospecting industry.

Although pulse induction detectors were available in the 1970s, they didn't gain much attention until the 1980s. These machines utilize a different technology that capitalizes on the phenomenon of electromagnetic decay. Instead of generating a continuous signal (like the BFO's, TR's, and VLF's), PIs use short bursts of energy to saturate the ground and any metallic targets contained within. Then, the receiver is "turned off" for a few microseconds allowing the conductive properties of the soil to "die down." Finally, the receiver is turned back on, thus detecting any metallic target that still has eddy currents flowing. Metallic objects like gold and silver will maintain their eddy currents for a longer period of time than the soil. Therefore, a PI machine is able to ignore a vast majority of the conductive minerals found within various types of soils while still detecting valuable objects like coins, rings, and gold nuggets.

They achieve excellent depth penetration and because they are able to simultaneously ignore both magnetic black sands and salt water, they are now the only type of detector used for working underwater. Strangely, it wasn't until the mid-1990s that PI machines began to be used widely for nugget hunting.

Table 10-1. The Nugget Table

Nugget Weight (grams)	Nugget Weight (pennyweight)	Nugget Weight (ounces)	Date Reported	Source	Notes
2528	1620	81.00	1860s	Many Sources	"A conservitive estimate of a nugget the size of an "Irish Potato" is 81 oz. (potato patch)
1568	1008	50.40	Prior to 1899	Blake, 1899	Reported as three nuggets worth $1008 with gold at $20/ounce
1555	1000	50.00	1870s	Many Sources	"A conservitive estimate of a nugget the size of a goose egg, using the method described for a potato (Golden Goose claim)
778	500	25.00	2000	Griffith, 2000	The "Tongue Nugget", which was found with metal detector by Jan and Jess Harkness near Stanton LDMA camp, March 2000
700	450	22.50	Prior to 1899	Blake, 1899	Reported as $450 nugget with gold at $20/ounce
700	450	22.50	Prior to 1932	Hosford, 1932	Reported as two chunks of quartz containing gold worth $450 with gold at $20/ounce
616	396	19.80	Prior to 1932	Hosford, 1932	Reported as $396 nugget with gold at $20/ounce, from Upper Weaver Creek
467	300	15.00	Prior to 1918	Watson, 1918	Reported as nuggets ranging from $150–300 with gold at $20/ounce
465	299	14.95	1999	Author's Observations	Found with metal detector by Bob K., Quartz-gold specimin that was par. of a 25-ounce patch of nuggets
373	240	12.00	Prior to 1932	Sawyer, 1932	Reported as "pieces over 1 pound"
323	208	10.40	Prior to 1921	Nevius, 1921	Found on the Octave Mine site in a placer deposit. Reported as $207 nugget with gold at $20/ounce
257	165	8.25	1918	Watson, 1918	Reported as $165 nugget with gold at $20/ounce. Found by Ernest (Gus) Reissman
252	162	8.10	1931	Wilson, 1952	Shaped like a molar tooth, 53 mm tall and 47 mm wide, contains 18.52 grams of iron-stained quartz, also contained 22.71 grams silver
237	152	7.62	1992	Author's Observations	Found with metal detector by Bob "Nugget" Gatowski
>156	100	5.00	1932–33	Wilson, 1952	Two nuggets, each one weighing over 5 ounces, Upper Antelope Creek
140	90	4.49	1998	Author's Observations	Found with metal detector by Chris Gholson
>93	60	3.00	1932–33	Wilson, 1952	"A few" nuggets over 3 ounces each, Weaver Creek
78	50	2.49	1995	Author's Observations	Found with metal detector by Chris Gholson
69	44	2.22	1992	Author's Observations	Found with metal detector by Bob "Nugget" Gatowski

A conservitive estimate of a nugget the size of an "Irish potato" would be 5x5x10 cm, which corresponds to a volume of about 131 cm³. Assuming a density of 19.3 grams/cm3, we get a total weight of 2528 grams, or about 81 ounces.

Rich Hill Electronic Gold Rushes—1970–1985

Very little information has been documented regarding the use of detectors on Rich Hill during this time frame, and even less is known about what happened prior to 1970. Nevertheless, metal detectors were most definitely being used in the district with limited success. One of these early pioneers was the American-made Garrett Groundhog, which came out in 1978. These VLF detectors, which operated at approximately 15.8 kHz, were originally advertised as coin machines until detectorists discovered their nugget-finding abilities. While the Groundhogs worked well on the North American goldfields, they struggled with the extreme mineralization found in Australia. Garrett responded by releasing a special model called the A2B. With its improved ground-canceling abilities, the A2B was better equipped to handle this mineralization and quickly took a commanding lead as the machine to use for hunting gold in the land "down under". The Garret Groundhogs are gone, but not forgotten. These venerable machines are still revered by many as the spark that triggered the modern-day electronic gold rush.

In 1983, Fisher Laboratories tried to capture a piece of the growing gold market by releasing their 660 Mother Lode. The machine worked well for larger targets, but the 4.5 kHz frequency was not conducive for locating small nuggets. Then in 1984, White's Electronics introduced the Coinmaster 4900/D, or 49'er. Essentially it was a meterless edition of their current 600/D line, with a few refinements specifically for nugget hunting. It became very popular among American prospectors and is responsible for finding many large nuggets throughout the Southwest. The author knows of one gentleman who detected several pounds of nuggets in southern California's El Paso Mountains with this very machine.

While these machines were designed to be nugget shooters, they were not much better than the coin machines of the day and would have been poorly equipped to deal with the adverse ground conditions found at Rich Hill. Due to their limited capabilities, only the large, shallow gold would have been found. Most of the nugget patches would go undiscovered until the late 1980s and early 1990s.

Rich Hill Electronic Gold Rushes—1985–1995

When gold sky rocketed to over $800 an ounce in the mid-1980s the gold mining industry began to buzz. Rich Hill, like many other historical gold producers, became a mecca of activity. It was during this era that the district saw more prospectors than it had since the late 1800s. One of the men there to witness this "gold" frenzy was Ron Driscoll.

"Things got a little crazy around the hill," Ron said. Droves of eager prospectors swarmed the slopes hell-bent on getting a piece of the action. Paranoid, gun-toting claim owners actively patrolled their property, as a warning to these would-be high-graders. Heated disputes over claim ownership, trespassing, and property boundaries were a common occurrence. Ron couldn't recall anyone actually being killed, but he said there were plenty of threats.

This mid-1980s activity was the first of the great Rich Hill "metal-detecting" gold rushes. Professional detectorists were now swinging the newly improved VLFs, and their old BFO and TR machines had become obsolete. These hand-held detectors were fairly lightweight, and compact. Once this new arsenal of machines was unleashed on Rich Hill, hundreds of gold nuggets began turning up. A few prospectors were lucky enough to find ones in the seven-, eight-, or nine-ounce range. The VLF detectors are responsible for locating most of the known nugget patches on and around the Rich Hill area.

However, if any one machine is to be associated with this time frame, it has to be the Fisher Gold Bug. In 1987 Fisher Laboratories introduced this 19.17 kHz nugget hunter. The super sensitive "Bug" gained tremendous popularity among nugget hunters and quickly dominated the Rich Hill goldfields. In 1988 Jim Straight, a geologist and author, wrote that "the Fisher Gold Bug is a classic in its own time. Its reputation as a nugget machine is legendary and worldwide. The Bug is a pure nugget hunter, capable of finding sub-grain sized flakes as well as the sought after big ones." The Gold Bug is still, as it was a decade ago, an excellent machine for hunting gold.

That same year Minelab Electronics, a South Australia–based company, developed a gold machine that automatically ground balanced, or compensated for changing ground mineralization. This was the 7.82 kHz GT 16000 Ground Tracker. The AGB feature made the 16000 very popular in the United States, especially in some of the highly mineralized Arizona goldfields, like Rich Hill.

In 1988, Compass Electronics came out with the 13.77 kHz Gold Scanner line. They were easy to use and attained good depth while still remaining sensitive to tiny gold nuggets. The Compass Challenger series came out shortly after the Gold Scanners. The improved X-200 featured a dual frequency (6 kHz and 14 kHz) function, which could be selected by flipping a toggle switch.

In 1988, an Arizona-based company by the name of Tesoro came out with their very first gold machine. The Diablo Gold Demon was a compact, nondiscriminating, and nonmetered gold machine to be used exclusively as a pole mount. It came standard with a 10-inch elliptical coil, although other sizes of coils were available. The Diablo was a well-rounded machine and achieved a fair amount of depth and sensitivity in areas of moderate mineralization.

In 1989, Minelab released the FT 16000 Fast Tracker. This detector was essentially a "souped-up" GT 16000. The newly improved electronics allowed it to compensate more quickly to changing ground, giving it a slight advantage over the GT.

In 1990, White's introduced the Goldmaster II, which operated at 50 kHz. At this time such a high frequency was unheard of. Perhaps as a result of this increase in operating frequency, the highly sensitive Goldmaster II was able to locate even the tiniest of gold nuggets.

A few months later, Tesoro released the 20 kHz Lobo. It was designed and engineered for finding gold nuggets. Sometime around 1991, Tesoro unveiled another gold machine, the Diablo II Gold Demon. Like the Lobo, it operated at 20 kHz, but was a substantial improvement over the earlier Diablo.

Around 1992, Compass came out with the Au 2000 and Au 52. The Au 2000 was able to utilize two separate frequencies, 14 kHz or 52 kHz. By contrast, the Au 52 was only capable of using the 52 kHz setting.

In 1995, Minelab introduced their dual frequency XT 17000 Extra Tracker, which allowed the operator to choose between a 6.4 kHz and 32 kHz setting. In 6.4 kHz mode, the XT achieved good depth and sensitivity toward nuggets of a penny-weight or bigger. The 32 kHz setting would not penetrate as deep, but was useful in locating small targets. It came standard with an 8-inch round DD coil. Its ability to cope with Arizona's high mineralization made it quite popular among local hunters.

Shortly after, Minelab released another product. This detector was called the American Gold Striker and had been designed specifically for American soil conditions. Like the XT 17000, the American Gold Striker featured Automatic Ground Tracking (AGT), which enabled it to automatically adjust to rapidly changing levels of ground mineralization. Its high operating frequency of 32 kHz made it extremely sensitive to flake-sized gold, even in highly mineralized soil.

24K Club

Ron Driscoll and his wife Kathleen arrived at Rich Hill around 1989. The couple was intuitively drawn to an area on the east side of the mountain known as the Devil's Nest. While scanning the remains of an old coarse drywash tailings pile with his Fisher Gold Bug, Ron picked up a promising sounding target. After removing several inches of rubble, he was rewarded with his very first piece of Rich Hill gold. Before walking away he made a quick sweep of the hole and was surprised to find that it contained another buried target. At first the culprit appeared to be nothing more than a bit of trash. However, upon closer inspection he noticed that it was actually an old 45/60 shell casing that had been ground down and fitted with a cork and rag stopper. After removing the cork he discovered the casing contained approximately 2 pennyweights of gold flakes. It had obviously been used as a makeshift poke and accidentally lost in the tailings pile.

Apparently Ron and his wife weren't the only ones sniffing around the Devil's Nest; in fact it was the most heavily searched area on the mountain. It is not known how this bajada deposit located in Sections 31 and 32 received its title. Some believe it derived its name from the abundant piles of hand-stacked, granite, boulders which closely resembled a bird's nest. How the word "devil" got thrown in the mix is unclear. Nevertheless, this unusual name has stuck to this very day. The historical richness of the "Nest" was part of the reason why people were drawn to it. However, it was the creation of the 24K Club that finally opened the floodgates.

The New West Prospectors Club was originally formed in Washington State, but eventually expanded all the way down to Rich Hill, Arizona. According to Ron, in 1991 the club had approximately 1000 active members. New West held claims in Arizona, California, Nevada, and Washington. Membership was $125 per year.

The overwhelming success of New West spurred on the formation of yet another club at Rich Hill. In 1991 the 24K (Karat) Club was born. It was essentially a spin-off organization and acquired a portion of the Devil's Nest property once held by New West. The 24K Club membership with its $150 down, $300 per year dues made it one of the most expensive recreational prospecting clubs in the Southwest. Claims, which had once been available to all New West members, were now off-limits to all those without a valid 24K membership. Many prospectors were outraged by the new changes, as they felt this was just a scheme to yoke them for more money. An overwhelming majority packed up their gear and headed elsewhere, never bothering to renew their membership. This severe drop in membership sent the club into an immediate downhill spiral. The economic pillars that had once supported this thriving organization crumbled, and like the Tower of Babel, it came crashing down almost overnight.

By 1994, the 24K Club had only eight paying members. Several months later it came under new management and with this guidance was able to make a remarkable comeback. In just one year membership swelled to over two hundred. The rejuvenated club boasted a variety of activities, such as dredging, highbanking, drywashing, panning, and of course metal detecting. There were also group outings, family BBQs, coin hunts, guest lectures, contests, and raffles. These were truly the good times and the club prospered. However, the one thing that set the 24K club apart from other prospecting clubs was its famous "dozer pushings".

In order to further assist the members in their quest for the gold, the club contracted a D-7 cable-driven bulldozer, owned by George Mead, to remove overburden from the claims. Every three weeks Mead would peel back several layers of earth, thereby exposing the virgin ground beneath. These "pushes," as they were called, were ideal for metal detectorists, as the VLF machines of the day could only penetrate

Figure 10-2. The 24K Club banner.

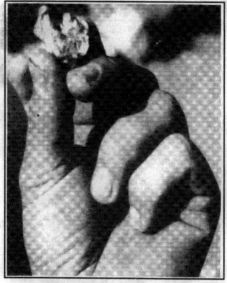

Wherever your interest lies
- Panning
- Dredging
- High Banking
- Metal Detecting
- Dry Washing
- Treasure Hunting
- Or Just Plain Fun

The 24 Karat Gold Club Has It All!

24K Gold Club
P.O. Box 574
Congress, AZ 85332

Figure 10-3. A 24K Club brochure.

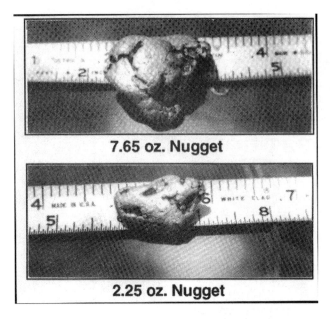

7.65 oz. Nugget

2.25 oz. Nugget

Figure 10-4. Two nugget pictures form the 24K Club brochure.

several inches into the highly mineralized soil. Removal of this overburden let the detectors "see" or punch deeper into the ground, allowing nuggets to be recovered that otherwise would have been missed on the surface.

After the ground was disturbed, there was usually a few days waiting period. Then on a specified date the members would gather and at the sound of a bell were turned loose. Ron said, "Sometimes there were upwards of 100 or more detectors buzzing around on the same push. It was literally a free-for-all!" The pushes were carried out in Section 31, and yielded some beautiful nuggets. The freshly scraped surfaces produced an average of ten to twenty nuggets per day, some being as large as one ounce! However, the largest documented nugget to come out of the pushes was a solid 7-ounce slug found by an Eskimo gentleman and his wife. There may have been others equal in size or bigger, but this is the only lump that can be vouched for by the authors.

The 24K Club pushes provided its members with hundreds of butter yellow nuggets over the years, but it wasn't just the members who were getting a cut of the gold. It is rumored that certain persons affiliated with the club occasionally indulged in what old-time prospectors had called "Sunday mining." Many began digging trenches by hand, others quietly moved corner markers, and a few even resorted to sneaking in at night with flashlights. It was even said that if any of the members got onto an unusually rich run of gold they were asked to move on, so that a quick cleanup of the area could be made. One gentleman supposedly removed over 4 ounces of nuggets before any member even stepped foot onto the fresh push. While the owners likely frowned upon this behavior, they chose to ignore it in an effort to keep the peace. Whether these rumors are entirely true is uncertain. However, it is probably safe to assume that

Figure 10-5. 24K Club members hunting after a push.

a certain amount of high grading was occurring. Despite all this, the members were able to enjoy themselves, and the camaraderie of their fellow prospectors, and find a little gold in the process.

Gold nuggets weren't the only treasures being found at Rich Hill during this time. A variety of historical relics and artifacts were recovered such as coins, buttons, mining equipment, bullets, arrowheads, bottles, and so forth. A prospector from New York made a remarkable discovery with his metal detector somewhere near the Beehive Mine. Several inches beneath the dirt he found an intact, silver bridle bit engraved with Spanish markings (circa 1800s), truly a spectacular find! Unfortunately he sold or traded this "one-of-a-kind" object before any photographs could be taken.

Another unsolved mystery is the *Oriental Horseshoe* also found sometime in the early 1990s. While horseshoes are not overly abundant, they are by no means rare. It was apparent from the size, style, and amount of oxidation that this particular horseshoe was quite old. However, its unusual markings set it apart from all the rest. Stamped on the back were the words "MADE IN JAPAN." How it got half way around the world and ended up on Rich Hill remains a mystery. The novelty was tacked up on the wall of the 24K clubhouse, but was stolen shortly afterward. The 24K Club no longer exists today, but remnants of the dozer pushes and the dilapidated building that once served as the clubhouse can still be seen.

Rich Hill Electronic Gold Rushes—1995–2002

With the development of the VLFs, the stage was set for bigger and better things. This is the era of the second great Rich Hill gold rushes. VLF machines continued to improve, but for the most part, the technology remained static and no significant break-throughs were made. In the mid-1990s, nuggets were still being found at Rich Hill, but with less frequency. When the 24K Club vanished from Rich Hill so did many of the prospectors. Consequently, the district's "detectable" gold production experienced a slight decline. However, this would all change with the release of Minelab's Super Detector.

You will notice that the following synopsis is slanted almost exclusively toward the Minelab metal detectors. This is not to say that other brands of detectors were not being used at Rich Hill during the late 1990s, because they most definitely were. Some of these include the Fisher Gold Bug II, the White's GM 3, White's GM 4/b, and the Garrett Scorpion Gold Stinger. These metal detectors are by no means inferior, as even to this day, they continue to be used by professional and novice gold seekers across the globe. However, their presence on Rich Hill was not as significant as the Minelab SD series detectors, therefore they will not be discussed in any great detail.

In late 1995, Minelab Electronics unveiled a remarkable new machine that com-pletely revolutionized the gold-prospecting industry. The Super Detector 2000 (or SD as it was commonly called) pulse induction detector made use of multi-period sensing (MPS) technology and enabled hunters to penetrate to depths previously unknown. The Australian-made unit was remarkable in its ability to successfully rework suppos-edly "hunted-out" ground. It eliminated virtually all the ground noise and troublesome hot rocks that had plagued the earlier VLF machines. The first hunters to hit the slopes of Rich Hill with the SD 2000 were rewarded with handfuls of shiny nuggets, some as large as 3 ounces. This was clearly the biggest detector breakthrough since the inven-tion of the VLF. Floyd Allen, a seasoned Rich Hill detectorist commented, "It was almost as if the hill had never been hunted before!" When it came to working the deep, mineralized nugget patches of Rich Hill, the older VLF machines simply couldn't com-pete. However, this rejuvenation was short lived. Once the known nugget patches were picked over the excitement slowly dwindled, and detectorists began to focus their efforts on Arizona's lesser-known gold districts and once again Rich Hill was abandoned.

Then in May 1996 the SD 2100 made its debut in Australia, but it didn't reach the goldfields of Arizona until early 1997. The 2100 was quite possibly the best-kept secret in the industry. Most people had been so impressed with the SD 2000 that they were reluctant to believe the 2100 could be any better. The price tag it carried was also a major factor, considering many had just shelled out a whopping $3,000 for the SD 2000. To give you an idea of how little attention this machine received, in early 1997 there were only about five operators using the SD 2100 in the entire state of Arizona.

Those who were willing to take a gamble quickly discovered the 2100 was incredibly more sensitive to smaller nuggets and penetrated even deeper than its sibling. Even those areas heavily searched by 2000s were yielding more gold. In fact, one of the authors was among the first to swing a 2100 over Rich Hill. In just three hours he was fortunate enough to recover a half-ounce worth of nuggets! Within a matter of months numerous pounds of gold nuggets were plucked from the hill, many weighing in the 3-, 4-, and even five-ounce range.

So how could the virtues of the 2100 have been kept quiet for so long? Most metal detector dealers still had money tied up in the 2000s and were not ready to invest in a new batch of machines, there was also a lack of advertisement on Minelabs part, not to mention the fact that those people who owned the 2100s did little to publicize its improved capabilities. However, like any good secret, it was only a matter of time before it leaked out. By late 1997 every professional hunter had heard of the SD 2100, and many were using them.

In late November of 1998, Minelab once again released a new detector, this time called the SD 2200D. This gold machine also utilized MPS technology and was ergonomically similar to the previous SDs, but boasted automatic ground balancing, improved tuning features, and a discriminator. The SD 2200D, like the 2100, was slow to take off. Despite these initial delays, the 2200Ds eventually filtered out onto the goldfields.

Since then, operators have uncovered a sizable amount of nuggets with it, probably the most famous is the two-pound "Tongue Nugget," found somewhere on the southeast portion of Rich Hill. The 2200D is an excellent machine for hunting gold, and is believed to have a slight depth advantage over the SD 2100 in some situations. Although many professional and amateur prospectors are currently swinging this detector across the globe, it has never attained the level of popularity once enjoyed by the SD 2000 and 2100.

Minelab's newest addition is the GP extreme. This pricey new detector is housed in a metallic blue case, and features automatic ground balancing, dual voltage technology, adjustable coil patterns, boost amplifier, soil condition switch, and a discriminator. Minelab claims that extensive laboratory testing has proven the GP detects up to 55% deeper on smaller targets and up to 18% deeper for larger gold nuggets than the SD 2200D. These claims have been hotly debated among prospectors in both Australia and the United States. Whether these tests are completely accurate remains unresolved. However, preliminary field test reports look good.

White's Electronics has also just released a new gold detector called the Goldmaster GMT that features AutoTrac and an improved discriminator. It is also rumored that Garrett will be releasing its own pulse induction gold machine sometime in the near future. Will these new detectors start another Rich Hill gold rush? Only time will tell.

Chapter 11
Rich Hill Today

Larry and Linda Walton are the current caretakers of Stanton, Arizona. Originally born in Illinois, the couple moved westward to California in hopes of finding work and a little gold. In May 1997 they relocated to Stanton, where they spent three years working as volunteers. It was during this time that Stanton was undergoing monumental changes. The original buildings were restored to working order and plans to install additional RV hook ups were made. Larry said, "It took every bit of three years before we could get those permits to go through." It was a long, tedious process, but well worth it. Stanton now boasts seventy full RV and trailer hook ups, water, a sewer/dump station, and telephones as well as dry camping for up to 125 people. Larry and Linda were hired on as the official caretakers in December of 2000.

Figure 11-1. Photograph of modern-day Stanton.

Stanton now consists mostly of motor homes, trailers, and several wooden and adobe buildings. Three of them, the hotel, opera house, and Butterfield Stage Stop, date back to the late 1800s. The opera house served as a bar, dancehall, meeting hall, and a place to conduct weddings. The Butterfield Stage Stop is where Charles P. Stanton was gunned down. It now serves as Stanton's main office. The most prominent building in Stanton is the old hotel. It was a place where weary prospectors and travelers could bed down for the night. It also probably housed a mercantile shop. The hotel is now used primarily for storage, a library, and pool hall. The other buildings in Stanton were most likely built during the 1930s to 1950s. It is believed that in the 1960s, some of the original structures in Stanton were torn down and used for firewood. Sadly, this is the fate of most ghost towns. Without the Lost Dutchman's Mining Association (LDMA) members and their efforts to preserve this historic town, it is likely that nothing would remain today.

LDMA members can stay at Stanton for up to six months. The cost is $5.00 per day for services. Gold Prospector's Association of America (GPAA) members are allowed to camp on club property, but only during scheduled outings. The LDMA has recently acquired 1480 acres of BLM mining claims to the southeast of Rich Hill. The Lucky Linda claims have produced numerous quartz/gold specimens and are open to both LDMA and GPAA members. The LDMA is currently in the process of obtaining the Pick'em Up claims, located about two miles northeast of Stanton.

Tips for Prospecting Rich Hill

Although the most productive areas of Rich Hill have been worked extensively by the oldtimers, there remains a considerable amount of gold still waiting to be discovered. Within the last two decades, the modern metal detector has enabled prospectors to successfully recover a tremendous quantity of gold that eluded miners during the original bonanza strike of 1863. Large gold nuggets have been found wedged in cracks and crevices, beneath granite boulders, scattered throughout drainage gravels, and amongst the tailings material ejected by early hand-cranked drywashers.

While gold nuggets have been found scattered in the plains and creeks surrounding Rich Hill, most of the larger pieces have been found on its slopes. A vast majority of these "big" nuggets never made it off the mountain but were instead trapped behind the abundant granite boulders. These natural obstructions, combined with abrupt changes in slope, slowed the gold in its downhill journey, promoting the formation of

154

exceedingly rich nugget patches. Some of the patches produced only a handful of nuggets. Others yielded many hundreds of ounces. When considering the historical richness of the district and its rugged terrain, it stands to reason that there are a good many nugget patches that have yet to be discovered. Electronic prospectors wishing to increase their odds of finding gold on the hillsides should be on the lookout for shelves, breaks, or other areas where the downhill slope has lessened. Gold is dense and relatively difficult to move without a consistent supply of running water. Therefore, when nuggets reach these "flats" they will have a tendency to stay put; thus the beginning of a patch. The prospector should also watch for shallow depressions created by the flow of winter and summer rains, as the gold will have a tendency to collect here as well. Larger waterways such as gullies, gulches, creeks, and washes should also be investigated, especially those with exposed bedrock. Rocks that have steeply inclined bedding, fractures, or cleavage provide an excellent surface for catching and retaining gold particles, especially when the bedrock "grain" runs perpendicular to the direction of water flow. Bedrock that has been polished or worn smooth is a less desirable area to search. Without an irregular surface to provide a natural trap, the gold will slip by. Therefore if time is of the essence, concentrate on those sections of bedrock that are rough and jagged.

Inside bends of waterways should be thoroughly hunted, as gold will certainly accumulate there. The reason is the difference in water pressure created whenever flowing water is forced to change direction. The centrifugal force causes a much greater flow of energy toward the outside bend, which creates a lesser flow toward the inside, thereby allowing the gold to drop out of the water.

Always search around the base of boulders, especially those that appear as if they have not been searched before. If clusters of boulders are encountered, it may be profitable to remove them and detect the virgin ground beneath. If nuggets are found, it could prove worthwhile to scrape away several inches of the overburden by hand and detect the freshly exposed surface. You would be surprised at how little material (or depth) it takes to completely mask a nugget from a metal detector. If you decide to do some digging, remember to backfill all your holes and restore the original appearance of the land as best as possible.

Also keep an eye out for stream-bed materials (rounded rock) strewn on the banks and hillsides. This older bench material now situated above the present-day creeks and washes was left high and dry as erosion took its toll and the waterways

Figure 11-2. Drywasher tailings. Note the distinctive signature of coarse oversize material to the front-left and fines to the right-rear.

changed course. These benches may harbor incredible amounts of detectable gold. If the material appears to have a reddish hue and is intermixed with black iron-rich stones you should most definitely hunt it!

Some other things to look out for in the field are workings done by the oldtimers (by oldtimer we are referring to the men and women who worked gold prior to 1900). Of particular interest to metal detectorists are the drywash tailings, mine dumps, and handstackings, which dot this historic Arizona landscape.

By far the most popular piece of equipment used in the recovery of desert gold was the drywasher. The first prospectors used or needed very little equipment, other than their eyes. These men would simply walk along and inspect the bedrock for exposed nuggets, as in the case of the Potato Patch. However, these rich surface bonanzas quickly played out, and the miners needed a device that could effectively process and recover coarse gold from dry gravels without the use of water, hence the evolution of the first primitive hand-operated drywashers. For a detailed history of drywashing, see Appendix A.

Fortunately for modern prospectors, the oldtimers didn't have access to metal detectors, so it is very possible that they lost quite a few of those prize bits in their tailings. It is for this reason that the coarse piles should always be thoroughly hunted. If you encounter a coarse pile, take some time first to grid the entire surface carefully. Then use a pick or rake to scrape down 1 to 3 inches and recheck it. This will allow your detector to gain additional depth. Continue this process until the entire pile has been leveled. Undoubtedly, you will encounter some metallic trash such as wire fragments, lead, staples, and so forth. Be patient and dig all your targets, because you never know if the next signal is going to be that multiple-ounce gold nugget.

As you might imagine, erosion has taken its toll on these old tailings piles. Some of them are moderately scattered while others have been completely swept away. Those that have survived may be overgrown with brush and can be very difficult to identify. Carefully scan the hillsides and banks, searching for anything that looks out of place. Usually they will appear as oddly classified humps, and with a little practice you will have no trouble identifying most of them out in the field. If you do happen to come across one of these drywashing sites, especially those containing older trash such as square nails, soldered tin cans, broken bottles, and tobacco cans, be sure to investigate them with the detector.

Also remember to detect the actual holes from which the material was removed. If the hole is not too deep, carefully climb down and slowly scan the sides of the exposed banks. Often nuggets can be plucked out of the walls. Other times prospectors will labor for days digging all the way down to bedrock and then forget to clean out the cracks. Herein lies a golden opportunity. Use your detector, preferably with a smaller search coil, to inspect carefully the exposed bedrock for overlooked values. One of the authors found four decent-sized nuggets in one abandoned drywash hole.

Hard rock workings such as mine shafts, tunnels, pits, and other exploratory diggings are another clue to watch out for in the field. They are usually easy to spot from a distance, and are a sure-fire indication that minerals are in the area. While it is unlikely that you will discover a gold vein by scanning the walls of an old mine, you may be lucky enough to find an overlooked quartz-gold hard rock specimen or nugget, if you know where to search.

The rock material removed from a mine was typically sorted into various piles according to its perceived value. The worthless waste rock (or gangue) was tossed out, while the ore was classified into low- and high-grade piles. Obviously the early miners were unable to assay the gold content of each and every rock, so much of the evaluation was done by hand. These hand sorters were highly skilled and had a keen eye for spotting high-grade samples. However, no one is infallible and eventually they were bound to miss a few. Hard rock gold can be completely hidden within quartz, or some other mass, and not visible to the naked eye. As a result, some rich pieces of ore were able to slip by unnoticed and cast aside with the waste rock.

Other times a mine may have been shut down before all the stock-piled ore could be crushed. Sometimes heaps of this potentially valuable ore may still be lying around near the mine. This is especially true of the gold mines operating prior to 1942, which were forced to shut down at the onset of World War II.

Remember, mines have dumps—mills have tailings. There is little chance of detecting a nugget or specimen within mill tailings, as all the ore has been pulverized into a fine powder. The dumps, however, are composed mostly of worthless waste rock and possibly pieces of ore that were considered low grade or accidentally mixed in. This material has not been crushed and it is here that electronic prospectors will have the best odds of locating detectable hard rock gold.

If you discover an abandoned mine it might be worth your while to investigate some of these dumps. However, before taking the time to hunt any dump you should be confident that the mine in question was actually a gold mine, preferably one which had free-milling ore. Free milling refers to gold particles that are not chemically combined with other elements within the ore, but rather occur as native metal. If this is the case with the mine you've discovered, then it's time to get started! First, remove any obvious bits of surface rubbish from the dump and toss them out of the way. Next, ground balance the detector on a section of the pile that is free of metallic targets. Then slowly scan the surface, keep the coil as low as possible, pack out any trash you detect, and always investigate any rocks (especially quartz fragments) that produce a clearly audible signal.

Some dumps are small, while others can be quite large. Trying to tackle a large dump at one time is often too difficult a task. To make the job easier, split the dump into imaginary sections and only hunt one area at a time. By limiting your search area you will have a tendency to be more thorough and less likely to miss targets. If you begin turning up some nice pieces of hard rock gold it may prove lucrative to clear

Figure 11-3. Mine dump.

away some of the dump material using a sturdy rake and hoe. This will allow your detector to gain additional depth and recover targets that would have otherwise been missed.

Any rock that produces a signal could potentially contain gold. However, rocks containing conductive minerals such as pyrite, chalcopyrite, and galena will produce a varying degree of responses on a metal detector. Most of the time these false signals are just the mineralization, and not necessarily gold. However, gold and these minerals are closely associated and are almost always found together. Just to be safe, you should save any samples that produce a distinct signal. Take them home and observe them under a loop or crack them open with a rock hammer. You never know, there could be a mass of gold hidden within the rock!

Another point worth mentioning is that any drainages within the vicinity of gold mines should also be hunted. Quite often, these gulches, creeks, and washes contain nuggets that shed from the original lode long before the mine was ever started. Even if you don't find any detectable nuggets, you might want to consider testing their "fine gold" potential with a drywasher. While mine dumps and their drainages often contain gold-bearing specimens and nuggets, they are notoriously trashy areas. Unfortunately for us metal detectorists, the oldtimers weren't exactly tidy with their rubbish. Anyone who has visited an old mine and had a good look around will probably agree with this. Nevertheless, be patient and don't give up too soon. Keeping your cool may mean the difference between going home empty handed or with a beautiful lump of gold in your pocket!

A word of advice, always use caution when hunting around hard rock workings. Many of the old mines have been left wide open and can be extremely dangerous. One slip and you could find yourself in quite a predicament. Stay clear of the shafts, tunnels, and so forth, and instead concentrate on the nearby dumps and washes.

Handstacking is of particular interest to electronic prospectors. Usually, this type of placer working can be found alongside washes and other drainage channels. As its name implies, handstacking consists of stacked rows or walls of rock. Once a gold-bearing wash was discovered the oldtimers immediately began removing the larger, worthless overburden in an attempt to reach the bedrock.

Gold can be found throughout the gravel. However, as the oldtimers quickly learned, the richer concentrations are likely to occur within 0.5 m of bedrock—either above or below the gravel-bedrock interface. Consequently, the rocks and boulders were pulled from the belly of a wash and stacked on the banks where they would be out of the way. Once this was accomplished the precious gravels found resting atop the bedrock were carefully scooped up and processed.

Moving large amounts of heavy rocks is no easy task, so whenever you encounter a hand-stacked wash you can assume it was fairly rich. The amount of stacking is directly related to the amount of the gold that was originally present. A simple rule to remember is, "The more stacking—the richer the wash!"

These hand-stacked walls can be nothing more than a few rocks scattered along a bank, other times they can be a towering ten-foot-tall wall. Unfortunately, erosion and modern mining activities have destroyed some of these stacked walls, making it difficult to identify potential gold-bearing washes. If you encounter a wash anywhere in the vicinity of Rich Hill, or any other placer area for that matter, with remnants of handstacking, settle down and do some serious hunting—there's bound to be gold!

Drift mining was also practiced at Rich Hill, most notably along the deep benches parallel to Weaver Creek. In places this material can reach an average thickness of 25 feet or more. Once again the miners were faced with a dilemma. They knew that the pay layers would be found near the bedrock, but how could they get to it without having to remove all the overburden? The problem was solved by tunneling into the side of the bench near the bedrock. Once the primary tunnel was established it was just a matter of fanning out into a series of smaller tunnels, working the rich bedrock all the while.

In many ways this method closely resembles hard rock mining, except nuggets are the objects of interest, not a lode. The loosely cemented gravel ceilings and walls were often shored-up with timber, allowing the expansion of an intricate tunnel network. The returns were high, but so were the risks. Cave-ins frequently occurred when large boulders broke loose, bringing down thousands of pounds of gravel with them. Foolish under-mining of support pillars and heavy rains may have also contributed to the cave-ins. Historical records suggest that Chinese miners are responsible for most of the underground placer tunnels in Sections 5, 6, 29, and 32. A search of these tunnels in 1998 by trained professionals with metal detectors produced approximately 1.2 ounces of gold.

If you happen to stumble across a placer or hard rock tunnel, please think twice before entering. The rotted timbers and pillars may no longer be capable of holding back the highly unstable overburden above your head. Several tons of dirt and rock may be waiting to crash down on top of you. The floors might be littered with disease-causing bat and rodent fecal matter. They could also be home to a variety of potentially dangerous creatures such as rattlesnakes and scorpions. Remember, your life is worth more than a few pieces of gold. There are plenty of other places to detect besides old drift and hard rock mines. So do yourself a favor, and keep out.

The Character of Gold from the Weaver District

Much of the placer gold that has been recovered recently at Rich Hill has a relatively high purity, suggesting considerable transport distance or exposure time. The authors performed many analyses of gold purity on samples they collected at Rich Hill. The average placer gold has a purity of 89% to 90% fine. A 1-g nugget from a Red Placer at the Devil's Nest mine was about 90.5% fine. Three small 1-mm gold grains drywashed from a young placer averaged 91% fine, whereas the under 1-mm gold from the same sampling was about 80% gold and 20% silver. Placer gold from Red Placers below the Octave Mine ranges from 90.5% to 92.5% fine, and sometimes consists of 1-mm-sized octahedral gold crystals. On the west side of Rich Hill, near the Helen Morris/Planet Saturn Mine, the placer gold can be quite silver rich, with some nuggets averaging as low as 78.5% gold and 21.5% silver. Other samples average 88% gold and 12% silver. Historical information indicates that Potato Patch gold averaged 92% gold and 8% silver.

Lode deposits throughout the district average 40% gold and 60% silver, and the authors' fire-assay of samples confirm this ratio for almost all galena and pyrite ore samples. While it is documented that the Octave Mine and many smaller mines produced many thousands of ounces of silver, there is no report of any native silver occurring within the district. The silver and gold occurs dominantly as inclusions on and within the lead sulfide mineral galena. Gold also occurs within the iron sulfide mineral pyrite, and the copper-iron sulfide mineral chalcopyrite. Lead and copper production from the entire district is reported at 747,610 pounds and 326,586 pounds respectively. For galena, pyrite, and chalcopyrite the gold and silver occur together as fine disseminations and fracture fillings within the mineral. It is clear from scanning electron microscope examinations that most of the gold and silver occur as 1- to 24-micron particles of one metal alloy within and adjacent to the sulfide minerals. The ratio of silver and gold in these particles and the corresponding production figures from mines indicate the two metals are alloyed together as the metal electrum. Minor amounts of gold-telluride minerals are also documented in the district, as is bismuth in traces. In the Octave Mine the pure galena assays 100 ounces of gold and silver per ton, the pyrite averages 8 to 25 ounces per ton, and the chalcopyrite just 3 ½ to 7 ounces per ton. Processing sulfide ores is very difficult compared to the weathered surface ores, and ordinary amalgamation with mercury will only recover a small percentage of this gold. Fine grinding and cyanide leaching is required to recover a higher percentage of the gold.

Appendix A
Drywashers and Drywashing Techniques

Drywashing is often the preferred method of processing alluvial deposits in areas with little available water. In its crudest form, drywashing consists of placing a small quantity of pay dirt on a blanket, where two people toss the dirt into the air to be density-sorted by the wind. The remaining dirt is caught on the blanket, and tossed again. When only dense minerals are left, the remaining material is further processed with gentle blowing and puffing by mouth. Another early method involved pouring pay dirt from one pan at about shoulder height into another pan on the ground while there was a breeze blowing. These methods, introduced to American miners and prospectors by their Mexican counterparts, are called *winnowing*.

A drywasher, also called a *dry jig* or *dry table*, is a more sophisticated device, similar to a sluice that uses air instead of water to perform the gravity-density separation of heavy minerals and gold from sand. In 1897, Thomas A. Edison designed a dry process machine for saving gold in New Mexico. Later, the Australian method of dry-blowing was introduced to areas like Quartzsite, Arizona and Manhattan, Nevada. They came in all shapes, sizes, and brands such as the "Mexican air jig" and the "Hungarian drywasher." Then in the 1920s, W. H. Harris first experimented with a hand-cranked continuous (blast) current of air. This ultimately resulted in the "continuous blast" type of machines still being used today.

In its simplest form, a drywasher consists of a grizzly (mesh size varies) supported by a frame (usually wood, aluminum, or steel), which is fitted with an adjustable riffle tray. Hand-cranked models typically use a system of bellows to move or vibrate the material across the riffles, while motorized models are equipped with a fan offset by a spinning counterweight. In this case, air is pushed through the hose by the blower motor, which then causes the unequally weighted fan to spin, effectively shaking the riffle tray. Basically all drywashers do the same thing; it's just a matter of how they accomplish it.

In a typical drywasher, pay dirt is shoveled onto an upper grizzly that usually consists of an inclined box covered with wire mesh or bars that allows material smaller than ¼ to 3/8 inch to pass through, while the larger oversize material slides off to be

Figure A-1. A bellows-type drywasher. This unit runs on a 12-volt motorcycle battery, and can also be run using a solar panel. Note the telltale signs of drywasher operation, the pile of oversize rock from the grizzly, (left) and the fine sand and dirt (right) from off the tail end of the lower box.

discarded. The fines that pass through the grizzly pour onto a second inclined box called the *washer box* or *riffle tray*. This hollow box has a cloth top covering, and cross-riffle bars that have a dip angle opposite of those in a water sluice. Modern drywashers most commonly use a "leaf blower" to move air through the washer box and spin an eccentric counterweighted fan blade, which shakes the box. In some models, the bellows are mechanically or manually manipulated to force air through the hollow box. As the air passes through the cloth cover, the lighter material in the pay dirt would be blown away or would slide off the inclined washer box, while denser gold and black sands would remain trapped behind the riffle bars. When the riffles are full of black sands, the washer box is removed and the drywashed contents, called *concentrates*, are collected for later processing by panning. A drywasher can typically process over two cubic yards of gravel in an eight-hour day.

As its name suggests, the drywasher was designed to recover gold from dry dirt. This is where many miners both then and now encounter problems. If the dirt is not absolutely dry (or at least very close to it) the drywasher begins losing gold. If small pieces of gold are intermixed with moist material (soil), they will have a tendency to slide over the top of the riffles instead of properly agitating down and becoming trapped. Larger nuggets will most likely be caught, but tiny flakes could be lost amongst the fine tailings. Shoveling dirt too quickly into the unit only worsens the problem. This causes the riffle tray to become overloaded and backed up with material, and once again the gold has an opportunity to escape. The only solution is to remove the dirt, allow it to dry under the sun or over a fire, and then run it slowly through the drywasher. As you

Figure A-2. A blower-type drywasher.

might imagine, this is a time-consuming process so many oldtimers and especially modern prospectors never went to the trouble of properly drying the dirt, but instead opted to run it through and take their chances.

Even if the material was completely dry the miners could not be certain they weren't losing large nuggets off the grizzly. It would seem that a 1-ounce nugget would immediately stand out on the screen, but this is not always the case. Drywashers produce large amounts of dust particles that can impair vision. The nuggets can be coated with a layer of dirt or mud, or encased within a chunk of clay. It would be easy for a nugget to slip by unnoticed, especially if a prospector were not paying close attention.

When in the field, make sure to look for the signs that indicate drywashers have been operating in the area. The drywasher usually makes a distinctive pile of oversize rock from the grizzly (*coarses*), while the *fines* from off the tail end of the lower box form a separate pile (see Figure A-1). Drywashers usually do not collect much of the fine gold content of the pay dirt, and oversize nuggets that pass off the grizzly are easy to overlook. Always make a quick sweep of drywashing piles with your metal detector. Drywashers, especially when improperly used, will produce delightful target-rich piles.

Recognizing signs of drywasher operation will also prevent you from spending hours processing "those wonderful piles of gravel that are so easy to shovel." Avoid running drywasher tailings through your washer. Instead, look for the areas that the previous drywashers were shoveling their paydirt from. Remember, you don't have to avoid an area because there are a few drywashing piles around. Contrary to being a bad sign, it just means that it was a good enough prospect for others to work, and if there are still gravels to mine you may be in for some luck.

Appendix B
Metal Detecting

Can you really find gold nuggets with a metal detector? The answer is, without a doubt, YES! However, there are a few things to consider before buying a detector and heading out to the hills. First of all, you must use the proper type of metal detector. Second, you must know how to operate it. Third, you must locate a gold-bearing district to begin searching. And lastly, you must be confident that the gold in this area will be of sufficient size to be sensed by the detector (i.e., large flakes and nuggets).

Choosing the Proper Metal Detector

Trying to decide which machine to buy can be a tough decision, because not all of them are well suited for electronic prospecting (or nugget shooting). There are basically three types of hand-held detectors available, each of them designed for a specific purpose. These are the (1) gold, (2) coin and relic, and (3) underwater machines.

Underwater detectors are only about half the size of a standard metal detector. The search coil and handle assembly are permanently attached to a smaller stem, making this type of detector too awkward to use on land. These machines are almost always outfitted with a discriminator and are not designed to be sensitive toward extremely tiny metallic objects. The internal electronics are also completely sealed and built to withstand the pressure exerted upon them as a diver swims about searching for sunken treasure. Since it is highly unlikely you will be searching the ocean and lake bottoms for gold nuggets, these detectors can be eliminated.

Coin and relic detectors were designed to search for buried objects such as coins, rings, and military artifacts. These machines are always equipped with a discrimination or reject feature that allows them to differentiate between ferrous and nonferrous targets. This enables the operator to "weed out" a large percentage of the worthless trash (i.e., nails and tin cans), while still detecting valuable objects. Discriminators are great for "coin shooting" playgrounds, beaches, and old historical sites where the sought after objects are at least as big as a coin. However, they are not the preferred mode for nugget hunting.

Figure B-1. Alyssa Gilbert with a modern coin machine.

The dilemma that gold prospectors are faced with is that discriminators invariably cause the detector to lose some sensitivity and depth. This is a not a major problem with coins, as most are only shallowly buried, and because of their flat shape, have considerable surface area. On the other hand, gold nuggets are irregular in shape and relatively small in size with limited surface area. Therefore, the signal they generate is often much less pronounced than their silver or gold man-made counterparts and can be easily masked or rejected by a discriminator. With this in mind, it should be readily apparent why prospectors will avoid using anything that will hinder their machine's capabilities. As a nugget hunter you will be searching for tiny flakes and nuggets buried in highly mineralized ground, so sensitivity and depth are two things you cannot afford to sacrifice.

Another problem is the type of soil found in gold-bearing areas. Prospecting for nuggets is not the same as "coin shooting" in a graded park or school ground. The ferrous (iron) matrix in a school or park is probably more uniform than the poorly sorted soil, sand, and rocks found within gold-bearing areas. Also, the park and school grounds were probably graded by machinery and the homogeneity was additionally assured during its development.

Since the magnetic ground matrix is generally more uniform in the weathered soils found in urban areas, a detector can be specifically designed or set up for "coin shooting." However, the diverse alluvium found in gold-bearing placer areas can vary greatly in chemical and physical characteristics. Thus, a gold machine cannot be preprogrammed at the factory. It must be able to quickly adapt to the changing ground conditions in which most gold nuggets are found.

Those models of metal detectors that are suitable for electronic prospecting must possess certain characteristics. These are:

(1) all metal mode
(2) adjustable audio threshold
(3) manual or automatic ground balancing
(4) interchangeable coils
(5) headphone jack

Nearly all modern gold machines will possess these features. Therefore your decision should also be based upon quality, reputation, price, customer service, and warranty. Take some time to research the available models and the companies that manufacture them. Scan the Internet, check out the advertisements in various gold and treasure magazines, but most of all talk with other detectorists. Find out which brand of detector other hunters are using, especially those who find gold on a regular basis. Chances are they wouldn't use a machine they didn't have confidence in. A metal detector can be a big investment, so take some time to find out which one is right for you. Here are a few questions to ask yourself before making a purchase:

(1) What is my budget?
(2) How often am I going to use it?
(3) Where am I going to be primarily hunting?
(4) Which manufacturer provides the best customer service and warranty?
(5) Which brand seems to be finding the most gold?

By answering these simple questions you can help assure yourself that you have made a wise choice.

Other Needed Equipment

Like any other sport, metal detecting requires a variety of gear. The area you are searching, your budget, and your own personal needs will dictate the type of equipment you use and carry.

After the metal detector, headphones are the next most important item. Some metal detectors are equipped with an external speaker, while others require the use of headphones. Most experienced detectorists will testify that headphones are better than external speakers. Headphones will enable you to hear faint or deeply buried targets, protect your ears from the sun, and keep out unwanted pests like flies and gnats. Headphones are also useful for eliminating much of the unwanted background noise caused by wind, planes, and so forth.

A decent digging tool is crucial for electronic prospecting. Picks come in a variety of sizes and weights. The larger, heavier metal picks make it easier to dig out targets in hard ground and pry up sizeable rocks. A larger pick will also allow you to dig a hole quickly and efficiently.

Along with your digging tool, you will want to carry a good magnet. The magnet will remove magnetic trash that may have set off your detector. A good magnet will save you many hours of digging through loose dirt, finding only rusty nails. Many prospectors stick the magnet to their pick for easy use.

You are also going to need a nugget pouch or container for your gold. Never use glass vials or jars! A plastic 35-mm film canister works well. The plastic walls won't shatter like glass if dropped, and they are soft so fragile pieces of gold won't be scratched or broken. A small piece of tissue paper can be placed over the top of the nuggets to prevent them from rattling around. Whatever you use, make sure it has a tight-fitting lid. There is an old saying about gold, "It's hard to find, but easy to lose."

You may also want to carry a separate trash pouch for the worthless items you will find such as nails, wire, bullets, pop tabs, cans, staples, and buckshot. Always try to pack out the trash you detect, unless it is too big. Extremely large pieces of trash like tin cans, metal pipes, and so forth cannot always be carried out. When you encounter items such as these, set them on top of a large rock or tree branch where they will be in plain view and out of the way. Never throw your trash back into the hole. If you do, you'll probably dig it up again someday.

Batteries can be unpredictable; it is for this reason that a spare set should always be taken on any prospecting outing. You don't necessarily have to carry them around with you, but you should at least have a fresh set in your vehicle. It would be horrible to get all the way out in the goldfields, only to discover your batteries are dead.

A sturdy pair of hiking boots is a must for any gold prospector. Make sure they have good tread and provide plenty of ankle support. Those without metal are the best because they will not interfere with your search coil as you walk. However, finding a decent pair of boots without metal eyelets is difficult. If your boots do have metal it would be wise to slightly extend the length of your detector's shaft to avoid any false signals. Whatever you buy make sure they fit comfortably; chances are you're going to be spending a lot of time in them!

If you have ever visited the Southwest in the summer you are probably aware how intense the desert sun can be. Despite being 93 million miles away from earth, the sun can have a powerful effect on your body. Ultraviolet light has been proven to cause skin cancer and has the potential to damage your eyes. Before heading out take a moment to apply sunscreen (preferably one with a high SPF rating) to the back of your neck, arms, ears, and nose. A wide-brimmed hat and sunglasses will help shade you from direct sunlight and protect your face and eyes when wading through thick brush.

An ample supply of drinking water is mandatory when prospecting the dryplacer areas of the western United States. Summertime temperatures at Rich Hill often exceed 100 degrees. Such intense heat can quickly deprive your body of this life-giving liquid. You should carry no less than two gallons of water in your vehicle, perhaps more. Drink frequently—don't ration it! Never wait until you feel thirsty because by that time you may already be on the road to dehydration. Wintertime temperatures are more pleasant, but don't be fooled, your body still needs water.

During the summertime, the Rich Hill area is notorious for its rattlesnakes. A number of species such as the Mojave, Western Diamondback, and Blacktail are known to inhabit its rocky slopes. While they are certainty beautiful creatures, a solid bite can be dangerous. The most effective means of protection is a thick pair of nylon chaps. There are several brands available, but those that come up to the waist are generally considered the best. They are available from most sporting good stores and prospecting shops.

The danger from rattlesnake bite has always been exaggerated, from the standpoint of both frequency and severity. Snakes are often viewed as being agressive, when in reality nothing could be further from the truth. Rattlesnake fatalities are *extremely* rare. In a U.S. Army Air Force Informational Bulletin of April 1945, as an indication of the relative unimportance of the snake-bite risk, the statement was made that there are more deaths in the United Sates each year from lightning than from snake bite; and that to a soldier, with shoes and leggings, mosquitoes are a thousand times more dangerous than snakes.

Rattlesnakes will avoid human contact at all costs. They will usually rattle their tails as a warning to would-be predators and try to escape. However, if continually harassed they will strike out of defense. Be cautious when stepping over rocks, lifting up boards and entering mineshafts, as these are favorite snake hangouts. These fascinating reptiles play a crucial role in maintaining the desert ecosystem and are deserving of our respect. If you have to shoot one of them do it with a camera—not a gun.

Nylon chaps also provide your legs with protection from the numerous species of cactus that inhabit the southwestern United States, such as the prickly pear and the dreaded teddy bear cholla. The "ball-like" joints of the teddy bear are covered with heavily barbed spines and will readily detach themselves on an unsuspecting prospector. They are difficult to remove from the skin, so avoid them. If you do happen to pick up one of these unwelcomed guests try using a pair of needle nose pliers or a long plastic comb to remove it.

Ground Balancing

Let's imagine for a moment that you have just discovered a nice looking piece of ground in a gold-bearing area. The surface is cluttered with an assortment of heavy, darkly colored stones and the soil beneath has a distinct reddish tint. In fact, it looks so good that you don't waste any time ground balancing, but instead flip the unit on and begin swinging the coil. It doesn't take long before your eardrums are flooded by a sporadic hodgepodge of sounds. It's almost as if there are targets everywhere. So, you proceed to dig down several inches on one of the more promising sounding targets. Strangely, the signal, which was loud at first, has slowly begun to fade away. With every inch the signal gets fainter, more dispersed, and harder to pinpoint. Eventually you discover that there isn't a buried target there at all, only an empty hole. Does this sound familiar? Anyone who has tried hunting in highly mineralized ground can probably relate to this story.

Metal detectorists often refer to highly mineralized ground as being "hot." When they speak of the ground in this manner they are simply referring to the various conductive and magnetic properties it exhibits, not temperature. The soil itself is not hot to the touch, but it can cause serious problems for a metal detector.

A vast majority of the goldfields are composed of rock, soil, sand, and clays that contain small grains of iron-bearing minerals. These minerals are predominately the iron oxides: magnetite, hematite, limonite, maghemite, and lepidocrocite.

Magnetite (Fe_3O_4) is a dense, strongly magnetic, black mineral. It is widely distributed in terrestrial rocks and is an important ore of iron. Magnetite is also the primary constituent of the so-called black sands that often occur in placer gold deposits. Because of its magnetic properties, this mineral has a powerful effect on metal detectors, even in small quantities. Hematite (Fe_2O_3) is one of the most common minerals you are likely to encounter on earth. It can be red, black, or gray in color and occurs in the form of rock or an earthy powder. This weakly magnetic mineral is often found in gold-bearing areas and is the most important ore of iron. Limonite is essentially a hydrous ferric oxide. This amorphous rock ranges from black to brownish yellow in color. Limonite is only weakly magnetic and is a minor ore of iron. It is abundant in the southwestern United States and found in most mineral deposits in a region containing iron-bearing minerals that have been subjected to oxidation. Maghemite (Fe_2O_3) is formed from magnetite or lepidocrocite by slow oxidation at low temperatures. It may also be formed by rapid oxidation of these minerals by a camp fire. It is reddish or brown in color and is often quite magnetic. Many hot rocks "sound off" because of their maghemite content. Lepidocrocite [$FeO(OH)$] is a yellow to brown gamma iron oxide hydroxide. It is formed under essentially the same conditions as goethite, with which it is commonly associated. Lepidocrocite becomes strongly magnetic when heated. It is also a constituent of many laterites.

All of these oxides exhibit a varying degree of ferromagnetism. Ferromagnetic substances can be magnetized by being exposed to another magnetic field, like the one produced by the coil. Materials (including the iron oxides, conductive alkali salts, ferromagnesian silicates, aluminosilicates, etc.) that allow current to flow will set up a secondary magnetic field. This often causes the detector to receive a signal from the ground itself that may be much stronger than the signal produced from a metallic target. It is this natural property that causes the ground in highly mineralized areas to become "hot". These false signals are referred to as "ground noise" and occur when a detector is not properly balanced.

Luckily, the mineralization of the ground stays fairly constant in a specific area, and it is possible to adjust the detector to eliminate most of the ground noise. This will allow you to distinguish a true target from the artificial signals produced from the ground. Typically, ground balancing is achieved by turning a control knob while pumping the coil up and down over the ground. Once the ground noise disappears or remains constant in both directions the detector is said to be "ground balanced."

Some of the newer gold machines have the ability to ground balance automatically. This feature, commonly referred to as AGB, enables the detector to compensate for rapid changes in ground mineralization by continuously adjusting the current balance. Some detectorists say they prefer AGB over the manual balance type, because it is easier to use and they spend less time ground balancing and more time hunting gold. The downside is that AGB machines often work too well, and will occasionally balance out very tiny gold nuggets if the search coil is repeatedly passed across them. This does not happen very often, but you should be aware that it is a possibility. There are also many hunters who still prefer the manual balance type of machines. They say that even though it takes a little more practice and time than AGB machines, the manual feature allows them to achieve a more precise ground balance. As with virtually anything, there are good and bad points with both. Regardless of which type of machine you are using, take the time to learn to ground balance properly, as it is essential for your detector to perform at its best.

Coil Control

The coil sweep is one of the most important concepts that you need to master in order to become a successful detectorist. If it is done incorrectly you will undoubtedly miss nuggets. The saying, "Low and Slow," is something that should be remembered while hunting. The coil (or search coil) should, at all times, be kept as close to the ground as possible, and should be swept in such a way that the coil is always level (or parallel) to the surface of the ground. It should never be swung in a U-shaped motion. A good hunter always overlaps each swing, ensuring a thorough search of the ground.

While out hunting, you will notice that the ground is not perfectly flat. You will undoubtedly encounter rocks, trees, cactus, shrubs, and so forth. Don't let this stop you from hunting, get in there and work your coil around the obstructions. When sweeping over large rocks, remember to keep the coil as low as possible. Swing slowly and follow the contours of the rock. Most detectors can penetrate right through a rock and will let you know if a target is buried beneath it.

Take your time. A slow, controlled coil sweep is crucial when searching for tiny or deeply buried nuggets. Don't forget to detect around the roots of trees and bushes. Roots make wonderful natural nugget traps, but please try your best not to damage the plant while digging a target. The coil sweep does take practice, but after a while it will become second nature to you.

Hot Rocks

Occasionally rocks, like mineralized soil, can produce false signals. Detectorists call these stones "hot rocks." Certain types of rocks that contain more or less iron than the surrounding soil will cause a metal detector to sound off. Unlike true metallic targets, hot rocks will not always produce a "clean" or uninterrupted signal when passed over with a search coil. Sound may be heard on the forward sweep of the coil, but none on the back sweep, or vice versa. The signal may also be distorted or broken in sound; you may even find it difficult to pinpoint. These are typical characteristics of many hot rocks.

Sometimes they can be ground balanced out, but often they cannot. The best thing to do is remember what the hot rocks in a particular area look like, that way you will be able to recognize them when you hit them. Be aware that hot rocks can mask gold nuggets. If you hit a hot rock and for some reason it doesn't sound the same as the rest, you should move it out of the way and check the ground beneath. A general rule is, if the hot rock is not too big, kick it out of the way. If it is a huge boulder or deeply buried, don't worry about it, because you will probably hurt yourself trying to move it.

You may also encounter false signals caused not from hot rocks or the soil, but from the actual bedrock. Some bedrock is so "hot" that it will sound as if you have lowered your coil over a large bit of metal. This will not happen often with schists, slate, or granite, but it is common in areas with volcanic country rock. If you get a signal and suspect that it is just the bedrock, you should check other sections of the surrounding bedrock to see if they also produce a similar signal. If they do, chances are it is just the mineralization. If the surrounding bedrock does not produce a signal, it could very well be an actual target.

It should be mentioned that not all rocks that produce a signal response are "hot rocks." They may in fact be meteorites. A meteorite can be described as any solid object from interplanetary space that has fallen to the earth's surface without being vaporized by frictional heating during its passage through the atmosphere. They vary greatly in size, shape, and appearance. Some are no bigger than a match head, while others can get up to several feet in diameter and may weigh over a ton. Most meteorites are irregular in shape. Many have shallow depressions, deep cavities, smooth pits (thumbprints), flow lines, and furrows. Recently fallen meteorites typically have a black fusion crust. However, oxidation and weathering may eventually turn the crust brown or rusty or destroy it completely.

Unlike gold nuggets, meteorites can be found virtually anywhere in the world. There is no rhyme or reason to where they will fall; therefore a thorough search of any location may yield meteorites. Unfortunately meteorites closely resemble terrestrial rocks and are often difficult to identify. Magnetite and slag are the most common "meteor-wrongs" found by detectorists. If you discover an unusual rock with your metal detector that looks out of place, take it to the nearest university for further analysis and documentation. You may find the extra trouble well worth it, considering some meteorites have sold for as much as $4,000/gram.

Digging Trash

You will quickly discover that metal detecting requires a decent amount of patience. One thing that tends to frustrate new detectorists is digging trash. Trash can be annoying, but rest assured, even the most successful detectorists have had to dig their fair share. The good thing about trash is that it lets you know how hard an area has been hunted. For example, if you jump down in a wash and start finding pieces of lead jammed down in the bedrock, then chances are no one has hunted it before. On the other hand, if you detect for a few hours and still don't find a single piece of trash, then more than likely it has been pounded to death.

Finding a sizable amount of trash lets you know that an area has not been hunted very well, if at all. So if there are any nuggets to be had, you can assume they are still there. Sometimes the best nugget patches have been bypassed because they are smack dab in the middle of a heavily trashed area.

Another thing about trash is that it can tell you if the oldtimers were in the area. If you begin finding discarded rubbish such as tin cans, buttons, square nails, boot tacks, and so forth, then chances are the early prospectors were in the area working gold. Remnants of abandoned campsites and rock buildings are just another indicator that gold may be close by.

After you dig enough trash, you will begin to recognize the different sounds it makes and will quickly be able to mentally eliminate some signals. The only piece of trash that is impossible to distinguish from gold is lead. This lead is most often found as bullets. Keep in mind that some items, which initially appear worthless, may actually be valuable relics. Things like coins, buttons, tokens, old musket balls, and mining equipment can often fetch good prices from collectors. However, you should take care to educate yourself about the antiquities laws that may apply to the removal of such objects. If you find something and are unsure of its value, take time to do some research. Check around on the Internet and local libraries and talk with other prospectors. You never know, that piece of trash may turn out to be more valuable than gold!

Pinpointing

Pinpointing a target is a relatively simple procedure once you get the hang of it. Your pinpointing skills will get faster the more you practice with the metal detector. The first thing to do when you hit a target is stop. Then, sweep the coil slowly from side to side, listening for the strongest signal. Now, turn yourself at a 90-degree angle and sweep side to side once again, listening for the strongest signal. You have now created an imaginary X on the ground, and the target should be somewhere in the middle of the X.

A target will sound strongest when it is directly below the center of the coil. Once you have determined the general location of a target you can begin to dig. Remember, most detectors need some type of movement (or motion) in order to sound off on a target. If you stop on top of a target, it will probably disappear, so always keep that coil moving when pinpointing.

Sometimes it is easier to pinpoint a target by turning the coil on edge and tapping it along the suspected target area. This is especially helpful for locating nuggets in bedrock cracks. Small targets can also be pinpointed by patting the coil around in a circular motion. To do this, first determine the general area the target is in. Then, gently pat the coil around the target until the strongest signal is heard. The target should probably be located just below the center of the coil.

Digging a Target

Gold nuggets only have a hardness of about 2.5–3.0, and are extremely malleable. They can be scratched, bent, or even punctured by a sharp blow. Therefore, if you get a signal and believe it could be gold, never strike that area directly with your pick. Instead, begin digging around the target, loosening up the ground. At first don't dig very deep, maybe a few inches, just in case the target is near the surface. Once this is done, use your hands or plastic scoop to pull the dirt out of the hole. Next, recheck the hole with your detector. If the target is still there, push the original dirt away from the hole and begin digging around the sides. This widens the hole and allows you to dig deeper without dirt falling back down into hole. Once again, pull the dirt out and recheck the hole. If the target is gone, it could be stuck to your magnet or in the dirt you removed. If the target is gone and it is not on your magnet, two things could have happened. Either it was just hot ground or the target has been buried too deep in the dirt you removed from the hole. Flatten the pile of dirt with your hand or foot and recheck to see if the signal returns. Occasionally, this will happen with very tiny nuggets.

Once the target is out of the hole you must remove it from the pile. Before you begin, make sure you are not wearing any metallic objects (i.e., rings, bracelet, watch, etc.). First, locate the target using the pinpointing methods already discussed. Then, lay your detector beside you and grab a handful of dirt from the pile. Run your hand slowly across the coil to see if you have the target. Most coils are equally sensitive on both sides, so it makes no difference if you run the material across the top or bottom of the coil. If you do not hear a signal, lay the dirt in your hand off to the side. Continue this process until you have the target in your hand. Now, dump half of that dirt into your other hand. Check to see which hand the target is in. Place the dirt without the target off to the side. Now dump half of the dirt containing the target into your empty hand, and check by running across the coil. Continue this back-and-forth process until there is only a small amount of dirt and the target remaining in your hand. You should now be able to see the object that set off the detector.

The back-and-forth hand technique used to isolate a target can also be accomplished using a plastic cup, Treasure Scoop, or plastic gold pan. These items may increase recovery time on small targets and protect your fingers from cactus thorns and scorpion stings. Experiment with the various methods to determine which one

Figure B-2. How to locate a target.

1. Pinpoint the target

2. Once target is out of the ground and into the pile, lay the detector down beside the hole.

3. Grab a handful of dirt from the pile.

4. Run the handful of material across the coil until the target is heard.

5. Dump the material back and forth between your hands, repeating step 4 until the target is located.

6. Open your hand and hope its a nugget.

works best for you. However, if you are using a VLF detector you may have no choice, as these machines can actually pick up the conductive minerals contained within your hand. Therefore, these plastic recovery tools may be required.

Digging a Target in Bedrock

Recovering a target from the bedrock can be a tedious task. It is amazing how deeply wedged nuggets can become, it's almost as if they burrow themselves into the bedrock! Occasionally, you can just look down and see a nugget lying on the bedrock. However, most require some coaxing to retrieve them from their hiding place. When you are hunting bedrock and get a signal, the target will usually be in a pocket or crack. The first thing to do is determine the target's location using the techniques previously mentioned. Then, remove any overburden (rocks, gravel, sand, etc.) with your pick or hand, and recheck the bedrock. If the signal is still there, remove any other excess material until nothing remains but the bedrock. Then bend down and blow into the pocket or crack, either with your mouth or a straw. Normally, this will clear away any dirt or black sand and expose the nugget. Make sure you close your eyes!

Figure B-3. Using a flat-head screwdriver to pry another nugget out of the bedrock.

If after this you still do not see the target, you can assume it is still hidden within the bedrock. This is where the screwdriver will come in handy. Use it to scrape out any cracks that remain, or to pry apart small chunks of the bedrock. Then use your hand to remove the material, and recheck the hole and your pile. You should recheck your hole frequently to save yourself from unnecessary work. Be careful when digging because it is easy to get carried away and lose a nugget. Use short, steady blows, and try to confine the material to the hole or immediate pile. Be patient, this can take a while. Fortunately, if you are digging up the bedrock and the signal persists, the chances of it being gold greatly increases.

Digging a Target on the Hillside

Digging a target on a hillside or steep bank can be tricky. It's bad enough that you have to worry about falling off the hill, but you've also got to dig this target and keep it from going down as well. There is a simple cure for this dilemma. First, pinpoint the target. Then, dig a shallow trench just below the target. Begin to dig the target by removing the first layer of dirt, pushing it down into the trench. The dirt from the hole will fall into the trench and hopefully so will the target. This simple technique prevents you from having to chase a nugget down the hill. Once the target is in the trench, you can recover it using the back-and-forth hand method already discussed. Always use caution when hunting steep banks. One slip may leave you with a broken leg or arm or worse.

Coils

The coil, also referred to as a search coil or head, is the device connected to the bottom of a metal detector. Its primary job is to set up and transmit the electromagnetic field. Coils come in a variety of shapes, sizes, and configurations.

Most coils are either round or elliptical, although experiments have been performed with both square and triangular styles. Round coils are used for general detecting, while elliptical ones can be helpful for getting up underneath brush and rocks. Shape effects depth and performance very little.

Coils come in a wide array of sizes depending upon which machine you are using. The smallest are often those found on the Fisher Gold Bugs, which are not much bigger than a silver dollar. Coiltek, an Australian after-market company, has begun producing extremely large coils, such as one 36 inches in diameter, for the Minelab SD

Figure B-4. A 36-inch diameter coil.

and GP detectors. Unlike shape, size will definitely affect the performance of your machine. Generally speaking, smaller coils find smaller gold, but don't penetrate very deeply. Large coils will locate big targets at greater depths, but aren't well suited for hunting small gold. Small coils (i.e., 8 inches or less in diameter) should be used to hunt shallow areas, such as exposed bedrock, or for working in tight nooks and crannies. They are especially good for hunting narrow gulches and gullies, or for poking around the boulders of Rich Hill. Large coils excel in deep, wide-open ground, such as that found in the outback of Australia. The disadvantages of a big coil are the weight, difficulty in pinpointing, and the overall awkwardness.

Most coils are either a monoloop (monos) or a double D (DD). Monoloop coils consist of a single circular winding of litz wire that acts as both the transmitter and receiver. Monos have excellent sensitivity and depth capabilities, but flounder in highly mineralized ground. Double D coils consist of two separate windings of wire that resemble two letter D's placed back to back. They are not as sensitive as the monos, but are virtually immune to ground mineralization. It is for this reason that DD coils are the preferred coil for working the highly conductive soils of the Australian goldfields.

The Mental Aspects of Nugget Hunting

Although many hundreds of nuggets are found worldwide each day, there are quite a few detectorists out there who have not been so fortunate. This situation raises the question, "Why do some hunters find gold consistently every time they go out?" Or more specifically, "What is it that gives them that winning edge?" Of course there are the obvious answers such as the amount of experience, the quality of the detector, a basic understanding of geology, or sometimes just plain luck. However, the answer to this question can be found by examining the psychological power of the mind. The four most important mental aspects involved with nugget hunting are confidence, patience, concentration, and motivation.

Confidence is not achieved quickly; it must be earned. It is the product of talent, training, and dedication. Confidence translates into power out in the field because you are absolutely certain of your ability. This inner certainty comes because you know that you know. It is a powerful force that can definitely influence your strength as a nugget hunter.

A good example is the fact that the first nugget is always the hardest to find. This happens in part because new detectorists have much lower levels of confidence than experienced hunters. They are unsure where to look and what to listen for; which leaves them feeling doubtful. Whereas experienced hunters know exactly what to listen for and are confident that if there are any nuggets within detectable range they will find them. The first nugget is by far the most important piece you will ever find, regardless of its size. It is truly an accomplishment that helps knock down certain mental barriers. It will remind you that finding gold is possible and that all your effort was well worth it. As your confidence increases, your faith in the machine and your own abilities will also grow, and from then on things will flow much smoother. In time you will gain more experience on where to hunt and the gold will be much easier to find.

Nothing destroys the chances of finding gold as much as a lack of patience. Patience is one of the most desirable qualities a nugget hunter can possess. A patient and optimistic attitude breeds success and is something that all nugget hunters should never lose sight of. First, work on the patience. Once you've mastered that, the skill and nuggets will follow.

A clear, focused head is essential to your success. Don't allow yourself to be sidetracked by other things going on in your life. Wipe the slate clean and put all your stress on hold. This is your time to relax and have fun, so don't worry about the phone calls you need to make or the doctor's appointments you have to keep. Try to forget all about your job and bills, even if it is just for a little while. Your only mission right now is to find some gold and have a wonderful time in the process.

Concentration is usually difficult to maintain, so occasionally you should take a break from detecting and observe your surroundings. The reason for this is simple; if you do anything for an extended period of time it can become monotonous and boring. It is easy to become hypnotized by the coil. This sounds funny, but after five or six hours of solid hunting your brain has a tendency to switch to autopilot. You become so fixated on swinging the detector that you become oblivious not only to what's going on around you, but you may also lose sight of what it is you're trying to accomplish. The point is, you need to take certain measures to avoid this dreamlike state; otherwise it will cost you nuggets in the long run.

This can be accomplished by taking periodic breaks throughout the day. Find a comfortable place in the shade to sit down and have a cool drink. While you are unwinding, reflect on the places you have already been and where you want to go next. Take a moment to examine the geology of the area. What do you see? What color is the soil, what types of rocks are there, is there any quartz nearby? Ask yourself, "Is this really where I want to hunt, or have I bypassed the best gold because I wasn't paying attention?"

Look around at the local vegetation. The oldtimers used to look for certain types of plants as an indicator of gold. A famous example is the unusual desert trumpet plant (*Eriogonum inflatum*), which typically grows in auriferous soils. You should also be on the lookout for any workings done by the oldtimers, be it coyote holes or drywash tailings. Staying alert to your surroundings will help you locate the most favorable areas for prospecting and help you avoid many potentially dangerous encounters with cacti, snakes, and other critters.

One of the most important motivational exercises you can do as a new detectorist is to make a conscious effort to learn more about the hobby. Everyone should be familiar with the basics, as it is difficult to progress as a hunter without a solid foundation of knowledge. Take time to read books and articles written by other prospectors, watch videos, explore the Internet, and freshen up a bit on the geology of placer and ore deposits. Always try to save any prospecting literature you accumulate because you never know when this material will come in handy for future research.

Another valuable exercise is to study the techniques of experienced hunters. These men and women have a lot of knowledge to offer, so listen to what they have to say. Watch how they adjust the detector and swing the coil. Take note of the places they hunt and the places they don't. Ask plenty of questions, but don't create an awkward situation by asking them the whereabouts of their "hot spots."

You might not know any other hunters, so sometimes you have to look for them. Occasionally they can be found inside prospecting shops, but usually the best place to meet them is out in the field. If you do happen to bump into one of them take a moment to visit or offer a cold drink, because you never know what you might learn.

Another important, but often overlooked, mental aspect of nugget hunting is that you should have a game plan before heading out to the hills. A very successful Arizona prospector once said that there is a big difference between metal detecting and prospecting. He explained that when you are looking for gold nuggets you are detecting, and when you are looking for new ground you are prospecting. His philosophy makes a lot of sense because there does seem to be a clear-cut distinction between the two. Having a game plan is important because it helps you to prepare mentally for your hunting trip. This may be another opportunity for you to maximize your chances of success while decreasing the level of frustration.

Here are a few things to consider when prospecting with a metal detector. Always hunt the most likely areas first. For example, if you are prospecting in a dry placer area you might want to check the small creeks and washes with exposed bedrock and the mesas between the gulches. Also, search areas at the base of a mountain chain where alluvial fans or pediment placers may be located. Don't waste time by hunting slowly (referring to the relative speed of each coil sweep) and only dig the obvious targets. This may seem contradictory to everything you have heard before, but it really does work. This is a new area, so your best bet is to cover as much ground as possible. It is all right to hunt quickly because all you're looking for is that one nugget to tip you off. Once you find it you can stop and rethink your strategy.

Detecting, on the other hand, is a completely different ball game. In this situation it is not a good idea to hunt quickly because you will probably be working ground that has already been picked over; like an old nugget patch. In places like this you are going to have to rely heavily on your skills as a detectorist. You must be totally focused on the ways in which you manipulate the detector. So, crank up your mind's sensitivity a few notches and turn your patience level to the max, because chances are all the easy gold is long gone.

If the area has really been hammered be prepared to go two to three hours without hitting a single target. This can really test you mentally because you will have to work that much harder in order to be successful. This may mean that you have to crawl through the brush and stick your coil into all those dark nooks and crannies that everyone else has avoided. This type of detecting probably won't net you much gold, but it will provide valuable experience, making you a better hunter. Tell yourself beforehand, "It might take a while, but I am definitely going to find a nugget." If you have the proper mindset, keep your cool, and stay determined, you will find gold that everyone else has missed.

When you are detecting places like this you should swing the coil at a slow to medium speed. Pay special attention to overlapping and keep the coil as low to the ground as possible, even if you have to occasionally scrape it on the ground. Don't listen for loud signals, listen to your threshold. This is especially true when hunting in areas with really deep gold. If a nugget is positioned almost out of your detector's range, it will not produce a clearly audible signal. However it will probably cause a slight disturbance in the threshold.

These disturbances will usually be a small dip or rise depending upon which type of machine you are using. Sometimes faint signals will be caused by ground mineralization, so when in doubt remove a few inches of soil and check to see if the target gets louder or disappears. If the target remains constant or gets louder, it could be a deep gold nugget.

One other point worth mentioning is that your equipment should always be adjusted specifically to your needs and be in good working order. Hunting with a bad coil or loose cable connection can make any prospecting trip a real headache. The night before you leave, look over the detector and make sure everything is functioning. Swing it a few times and set the shaft to a comfortable level so that you're not having to hunt slumped over. Also, try to always use your own equipment, like headphones. After using a certain pair for a while your ears become accustomed to them and might be less responsive to another set. Hunting with unfamiliar equipment might dull your senses and cause you to miss nuggets that you normally would have found.

Clean your detector. Use a damp cloth to get rid of the dust and mud. A little bit of dirt on the box or coil won't necessarily affect its performance, but it might affect yours. Have you ever noticed that your car or truck seems to run better after giving it a thorough washing? Of course the vehicle doesn't actually run any better than it did before the washing, but psychologically it feels like it does. Well, the same thing holds true for your metal detector. That is why maintaining a clean, shiny coil and control box can be beneficial. It suggests that the machine is working in tip-top shape and provides you with a new sense of confidence. Your mood will have a tendency to remain pleasant and the chances of success will be high. Taking the time to properly care for your equipment will not only make you feel and hunt a whole lot better, but will also prolong the life of your machine.

If you spend much time at all out in the field, you will quickly realize that metal detecting for gold is just as much a mental game as it is physical or technical. It is a real sport that requires patience, enthusiasm, concentration, and a willingness to work. However, once you learn to "ground balance" your mind, all the pieces of the puzzle will come together and success will be waiting for you around every corner!

Appendix C
Desert Survival and Hazard Recognition

General Information

The desert environment of the Stanton-Rich Hill area is harsh, and has claimed many lives. Do not underestimate the power of the desert to harm you. However, with the proper precautions, your visit can be pleasant.

This section is presented as a brief outline of logical steps to consider when faced with the dangers of the desert and is designed for rapid decision making based upon some pre-planning and awareness of the likely hazards. No medical claims are made here, and there is no substitute for seeking advice for your specific questions from competent, trained medical professionals. Use common sense and remember that the ultimate responsibility for your safety lies in your ability to adequately educate and prepare yourself for travel in the desert. Above all, take plenty of water with you, and seek immediate professional medical attention for any injury.

Water and Sun

One of the ironies of the desert is that most of the time there is not enough water, and yet with a single cloudburst there can be too much. Always carry at least three quarts of water during the hot summer months, and in the winter at least one quart of water. If you think that you don't need to take water with you, or that you don't need so much water, remember that the one time that you do need it, it will save your life. Regardless of whether you are thirsty or not, try to take at least a small drink (gulps, not small sips) of water every thirty minutes or so. If you wait until you are very thirsty, you are putting unnecessary stress on your body. Avoid relying upon caffeinated beverages such as coffee and cola to slake your thirst. Caffeine is a diuretic, and will usually force you to urinate away more fluid than you consumed in the first place! And while a cold beer might be perfect around the campfire at night, there is no place for alcoholic beverages before or during a day hike. Alcohol is a diuretic, and will dehydrate you just like caffeine.

Dehydration is often a sneaky disorder. It doesn't really matter what time of the year it is: in the hot summer months you will lose a lot of water, but you will also lose a lot in the cool but dry winter with every breath you exhale. The early symptoms of dehydration are often overlooked when hiking or performing strenuous chores such as digging. Thirst is not always a reliable indicator, as small sips of water or chewing gum can mask the degree of real thirst. The early symptoms often include flushed or red skin, loss of appetite, irritability, and slowing down. Of course these things can easily be falsely attributed to having dug up the twentieth piece of trash during the day's metal detecting! When you have lost enough water that you notice the more advanced symptoms of dehydration such as nausea, vomiting, dizziness, headache, and slurred speech, you are in serious trouble. At this stage you need water to replace that which has been lost, regardless of how nauseous you feel. Seek medical attention. Remember that there is no need to allow things to get this out of hand. Prevention is the best medicine, and if you drink plenty of water during the day (at least a couple quarts), you will probably be fine and avoid dehydration in the first place.

Heat stroke is another potential killer to watch for. In hot weather with physical exertion your body's cooling systems may overload and shut down. If the evaporation of sweat is not sufficiently cooling the body and you overheat, you may stop sweating. Your skin will flush and become dry. Next you collapse, and without treatment you may die. Obviously you should avoid having to treat heat stroke by preventing it. Keep your body temperature low by limiting physical activity in proportion to the increasing temperature (hotter means go slower). Also wear loose clothing to keep the sun off, drink plenty of water, and take breaks in the shade if available. If you sweat out too much salt, you may also get heat cramps. Your body salts (called electrolytes) serve to conduct the electrical impulses of muscle and nerve, and if depleted you may have painful cramps. Luckily the "normal" American diet is quite high in salt, but taking along a few salted crackers or salt tablets may be wise just in case. Again, always seek immediate medical attention if you suspect anything is wrong.

Lastly, make sure to cover up with a wide-brimmed hat, loose-fitting clothes, and apply sunscreen to exposed skin. Always reapply sunscreen when sweating, even if it is supposed to be water resistant. Sunburn is not only painful, but is linked to skin cancer. Remember the stereotypical image of the desert prospector? He has loose-fitting long pants and long-sleeved shirt and a hat with a large floppy brim for a reason! A little sticky sweat and sunscreen washes off at the end of the day, but unpleasant sunburn lingers much longer.

Strangely, the wet and cold can also be a killer in the desert. Hypothermia (often called exposure) is the main problem to be aware of. If you are wet from sweat or rain and a breeze is blowing, Even if it is not too cold, you are at risk of hypothermia as your body is having its heat "whisked" away faster than it can generate it. You may start to feel very cold and begin shaking uncontrollably. Shaking and shivering is your body's signal to fire up the muscles to generate more heat. Put on dry clothes if you have them, get out of the wind, and if a fire, warm drinks, or other heat source is not available, start burning calories with physical activity. If you wait too long to warm and dry yourself your body may loose the ability to rewarm itself. At this point you will slow down mentally and think that you are warming up while at the same time you begin to feel sleepy. At this stage you need heat from an external source such as a fire or another person's body. Again, an ounce of prevention is worth a pound of cure. Prevent hypothermia by staying dry and out of the wind.

Getting Lost

Yes, it can happen to even the most experienced field hand. You are looking down at your metal detector and after digging your last target you look up to find that you don't have any idea where you are! Carry topographic maps and a compass, and know how to use them. There are many excellent books available on orienteering (map and compass use). A Global Positioning System unit, or GPS, is also an invaluable tool that costs as little as $100. But remember that you are vulnerable if this is your only orienteering device and the unit breaks or batteries go flat.

Always tell others where you will be going, and when you will return. Also, plan an "escape route" before the day's work. Look at a map and come up with a simple and easy way to remember the route or landmark that will get you home. For example, "I can always go south and will intersect the east-west dirt road that leads to camp," or "look for the power poles and then follow them away from the hills toward the paved road." Always park in a conspicuous location that will be easy for you to see from a distance. Parking in the bottom of a dry wash not only runs the risk of flash-flood damage, but also the frustration of spending the end of the day searching through many look-alike washes for your hidden car.

If you get lost, the most important thing to do is remain calm. Do not give in to the temptation of running up and down hills to look for a landmark. Conserve energy and don't wander far. Many people who are lost will unknowingly wander away from search parties and home. If you are lost, just striking out on foot will not help, especially if you do this in the heat of the day. If you think you might be lost, evaluate your situation without letting your ego get in the way. There is no shame in being lost. If you have plenty of water and have no medical emergency, find shade and evaluate your situation. Look around the surrounding countryside for man-made landmarks. By now it is probably late in the day, and the sun will be setting in the west, which will give you a reference direction. Collect wood, leaves, brush, or anything that will burn. By the time it is dark, you will have a good idea how lost you may be. Scan the horizon for any man-made lights, as it is often difficult to see buildings and power poles from a distance by day, but by night they will be beacons of hope.

Now is the time to start signaling for help. Light a big fire, but don't set the whole desert ablaze. If you are in an area where you think your fire might be mistaken for a campfire, light three smaller fires. In addition to signaling, fires are good to keep you warm and occupied. Packing a loud whistle with your gear is a good idea, and this might be the time to try it out. Any loud noise in sets of three is a universal distress signal, and noise travels farther in the still of the night. Don't overdo it and exhaust yourself though: signaling with three blasts every fifteen minutes is a good interval .

If you have left a plan with someone else, they will worry when you are late. Search parties in the night with headlights or flashlights will probably be as easy for you to locate, as your fire will be for them. If the decision is made to start the search in the morning, your fire will still help you. In the morning hours try placing green scrub brush on the fire to make a column of thick, dark smoke. Don't sit and sulk about your situation: Make a big fuss to draw attention without tiring yourself out, and don't be shy! If you stay put so your rescuers won't be searching for a moving target, and make yourself easier to find with a signal, you will have the best chance for a safe return.

Emergency Kit

Always carry a small emergency kit in your gear. This should include a reliable fire starter (lighter), loud signal whistle, extra water bottle (full!), a small first-aid kit, and any other items you feel would be useful such as a pocket knife. You should also consider packing a small bottle of extra sunscreen.

Poisonous Animals

Rattlesnakes—The Weaver-Rich Hill District is home to many rattlesnakes, the most common species being the Mojave and Western Diamondback rattlesnakes. The Rich Hill rattlesnake season is February and March, and it is the worst time to be bitten as the snakes are full of venom, out of hibernation, and ready to hunt. However, be prepared for rattlesnakes at any time of the year.

According to the U.S. Food and Drug Administration, "about 8,000 people a year receive venomous snake bites in the United States, and only 9 to 15 victims die: more people die from wasp and bee stings than from snake bites." About 80% of those bitten are men aged twenty to fifty. Many bites involve alcohol consumption, and that is not because the snake has been drinking! Ninety percent of bites result from careless behavior, such as picking up a snake, poking it with a stick, or other senseless provocation. About 10% of bites result from people stepping on a snake, not being careful where they put their hands and feet, or other legitimate accidental encounters. What these statistics should tell you is that by using vigilance and common sense, your chances of being bitten by a snake are quite low. After all, why would a snake want to bite something as big as you, and probably be killed for doing so?

Use extreme caution when working around old hand-stacked rock piles. There is probably at least one snake, as well as other potentially nasty critters inside each pile. If you will be performing high-risk work, like moving hand-stacked rocks, wear snake chaps, snake gauntlets (special bite-resistant garments), and other protective gear: always be on guard. A good rule of thumb is to never put your feet or arms into any place that you can't see, including overhead ledges and holes.

If you hear the distinctive "buzz-rattle" warning of a rattlesnake, try your best to be perfectly still. You have frightened the snake into a defensive posture, and you should wait for it to calm down and then slowly back up. Sudden movements will only provoke the snake, and it will move far faster than you. Look for the snake, and wait for it to leave. It is frightened, and will probably move away as soon as it feels safe. Remember that you should be at least a body length (its length, not yours!) away from the snake, as snakes can strike a distance of at least one-half their body length.

If bitten by a rattlesnake, the most important thing to remember is to get away from the snake before you are bitten a second time, and stay calm. Do not attempt to kill the snake, as that is a good way to turn one snakebite victim into two. Remove any jewelry from bitten areas as swelling may later make this a problem, especially with

192

rings. Monitor for symptoms of shock and be prepared to administer appropriate treatment. Most health-care professionals suggest following at least the following basic steps following a snakebite:

(1) Wash the bite with soap and water or antiseptic.

(2) Immobilize the bitten area and keep it lower than the heart.

(3) Get medical help.

Immediately seek medical attention! It is best not to try the "old method" of cutting at the wound and attempting to suck out the poison. Your chances of hitting a vein, artery, or major nerve are too great compared to the small benefit. The use of a suction-type venom extractor pump may be useful if available and directions are followed. If you are unable to get the victim to medical care within thirty minutes, a loose bandage (e.g., bandana) placed two to four inches above the bite may help slow movement of the venom. This bandage should not cut off blood flow from a vein or artery, and should be loose enough that a finger can slip under it. Get to a hospital as soon as you can. After the venom has been in the wound for a few hours you will have lost an important opportunity for effective treatment and have greatly increased the odds of long-term complications. Once you get the patient to a hospital, they may administer antivenin to counteract the snake venom.

Scorpions are common as black and brown varieties and are generally ¼ to 2 inches long. Always use caution when picking up rocks, as scorpions often cling to the bottom side. The sting is comparable to a wasp sting. Ice the sting location and clean the wound with antiseptic to guard against infection. Some individuals have an allergic reaction to stings, and at the first sign of shock, reduced breathing capacity, or lightheadedness you should seek professional medical treatment.

The **centipede** has one set of poison fangs in the front of its head. Bites are very painful, and should be treated by icing the sting location and cleaning the wound with antiseptic to guard against infection. Watch for allergic reaction as stated above for scorpion stings.

The **black widow spider** is very poisonous, is about the size of a pea, and has a shiny black body with a red "hourglass" or "figure eight" mark on its belly. If bitten, seek immediate professional medical treatment. The bite is often excruciatingly painful, but with treatment is seldom fatal (only four deaths have been reported in the past ten years). Antivenin can be given to reduce the pain and shock. The drawback is that present antivenin is usually only effective once, and will not work well for future bites.

The **gila monster** is a venomous lizard up to 60 cm long (about 2 feet), with multicolored orange-yellow-red-black skin with many raised bumps. We know of no fatalities from this type of bite, and few bites are reported. Unlike the rattlesnake, these lizards are slow and difficult to provoke: most bites result from playing with a gila monster. The gila monster is a protected species and killing one carries a stiff penalty, even if it was killed when you removed it from your hand. Leave these lizards alone, and you will have no trouble. In the off-chance that you experience a bite, seek professional medical treatment. The saliva is the venom, and it penetrates much more slowly than snake venom.

The **tarantula** spider is a particularly fearsome looking "hairy" spider up to 14 cm (about 6 inches) from leg to leg. It usually has a distinctive dark brown to orange color, and will rear up on its back legs and hiss when threatened. Most bites are of the "careless hands" variety (see rattlesnake section), or the result of playing with a spider. The bite, while painful, is usually not dangerous except for young and old persons, and those with an allergic reaction. Seek medical attention, and keep the wound clean to prevent infection.

Painful Plants

For a comprehensive, well-illustrated, and very readable book on cacti and other desert plants, we recommend picking up a copy of Reg Manning's *What Kinda Cactus Izzat?* It goes without saying that you should be careful what plants you brush up against, and be cautious when selecting a seat. It is wise to carry a pair of tweezers to remove small cactus spines, and either an old comb or pliers to remove cholla balls. Any encounters with prickly desert plants should be treated by removing the offending spine or needle, and then cleaning the wound with antiseptic to prevent infection.

Remember that it is a crime to disturb or remove cacti from the desert. Please leave all desert plants alone for the enjoyment of others. Desert plants, while painful for those who are careless, are not a major danger. We are only aware of a few fatalities, all of which resulted from folks who were crushed by saguaro cacti that they were chopping down. A saguaro cactus is mostly water, and can weigh over a ton!

Appendix D
Claims, Land Use, and Legal Status

Claim Staking in the Early Days of the District

The Rich Hill-Weaver District has a complex history of landownership status and regulation. In the early days, claim staking and legalities were governed by common-law procedure. In a new district such as the Rich Hill-Weaver District, a recorder would be elected and paid by the miners to oversee claim registration and adjudicate any disputes. For specific disputes, the involved parties might ask for referees to be elected and judge the case. In smaller camps, and for the most serious offences, a miners' meeting might be called to determine the outcome and punishments.

The discoverer of a placer or lode deposit would gain possession of a portion of the newfound prospect, called a "claim", the size and shape of which would be determined by the local mining committee. The claim would be marked at the corners by the owner, who would erect posts or stone piles called "cairns." A claim notice would be written, and posted at the center of the claim. Lode claim notices usually took the form of:

> Notice: We the undersigned claim three claims, of three hundred feet each, on this gold-bearing quartz lead or lode, extending north and south from this notice, with all its dips, spurs, and angles, variations and sinuosities, together with 50 feet of ground on either side for working the same.

Placer claim notices at Rich Hill were similar, but the claims were often much smaller in size due to their exceptional richness and the fact that many were centered upon stream channels. In some of the richest areas, claims were defined by the reach of one's shovel from the center of the claim. For both lode and placer claims, a similar notice with the location of the claim had to be presented within thirty days to the district recorder. Each person had the right to one claim, and with a lode claim a mill site claim might also be filed. As a courtesy to those who found a new district, a second claim, called a "discovery claim", could be staked by those involved in the find.

Within a ninety-day period, the claim owner must perform $100 worth of assessment work to prove the claim economically viable. Every year thereafter, an additional $100 worth of work was required. Claims where assessment work was not performed on time, or where not occupied and therefore deemed abandoned by the recorder, were open to new ownership and registration.

Modern Land Use and Regulation

At the time of this writing, the laws governing mining and even casual hobby prospecting on public lands are quite complex. As the legal concerns regarding these issues are in a constant state of flux, we cannot provide specific details concerning mining law and land use. Instead, we provide some general information that may prove to be of some assistance in negotiating the labyrinth of government agencies and regulations. However, you should be aware that this information is not the final word, and will certainly change over time, especially with regard to the major efforts underway that are intended to "modernize" the existing mining laws.

Virtually every square inch of the Rich Hill District is still under claim, and you should always check ownership status before doing any prospecting or metal detecting. Land ownership and mineral rights (claims) are often separate at Rich Hill. There are lands under private ownership, state lands, and Bureau of Land Management (BLM) lands. The public lands can be accessed and used by hikers and campers under the regulations imposed by the controlling governing agency. Separate from land ownership are the mineral rights, and often the holders of mineral rights and prospecting permits do not have the right to prohibit the public from accessing these lands for recreational use other than prospecting. Private landholders who also hold mineral rights have control over all activity on the land.

Permits for mining operations and prospecting are fairly straightforward, but the exact permit needed and the particulars regarding use are best left to the appropriate government agency. It is suggested that land ownership and mineral rights be investigated by contacting:

Arizona State Land Department
Public records (602) 542-4631
Minerals Division (602) 542-4628

Bureau of Land Management, Arizona State Office
222 N. Central, Phoenix, Arizona 85004
(602) 417-9528

Arizona Division of Mines and Mineral Resources
1502 W. Washington, Phoenix, Arizona 85007
(602) 255-3795

The Arizona Division of Mines and Mineral Resources (ADMMR) offers two publications, Special Reports 11 and 12, that will help you determine land status and understand federal and state mining laws. Details on how to order these and other related publications can be obtained by contacting the ADMMR at the above address, or by accessing their website at:

www.admmr.state.az.us

The ADMMR is also a valuable source of information on general mining, and it has an excellent mining library with extensive holdings of land-status maps, topographic maps, and geologic maps available for public reference. As of this writing, photocopies of ADMMR documents can be made for a small fee per copy, but documents cannot be checked out of the library.

Appendix E
Additional Hard Rock Mines of Rich Hill

While this listing of mines is fairly comprehensive, it does not cover every individual prospect hole. In many cases the diggings of an area are grouped together under the name of the largest property or mine. For an overview of the location, commodities, production history, and discovery dates we refer you to the mine location and commodity tables in chapter 6. Some important mines within the Martinez District such as the Congress Mine and Marcus Mine lie outside of the immediate Rich Hill area covered in this book, and are not covered in this book

War Eagle Mine

The War Eagle is unusual in that it is both a lode and placer mine. Located on the Patsy Group claims, it was owned and operated from 1939 to 1946 by Frank Gillick. Operations were interrupted by the war years, but several minor workings were developed. On the alluvial claims, a 32-foot shaft was sunk on gravels that averaged 0.006 to 0.03 ounces of gold per cubic yard. The lode mine is centered upon a 2-foot-wide vein that reportedly averages 0.2 ounces of gold per ton. A 60-foot-deep shaft follows this vein, and only a few tons of ore have been mined, yielding less than 20 ounces of gold. The shaft is filled with water to within about 20 feet of the surface.

Myers Mine

The Myers Mine is centered upon a fault vein of quartz with gold-bearing pyrite, and lesser amounts of gold-rich galena, sphalerite, and chalcopyrite. This vein strikes 60° east of north for about 500 feet, dips 30° to the northwest, and is 1 to 3 feet thick.

George Myers owned the seven claims covering the deposit, and in 1934 formed the Consolidated Mining and Development Company. This company operated the mine for the main productive years of 1934 to 1947 under the direction of Myers, and later on leased by the company directors George Long, Heying, and Pomeray. The mine managers for this period were Leo Rickwalt and later Dr. E. C. Hagood.

Development of the property started in 1934 with the sinking of the main inclined shaft. This shaft was inclined at 30° and followed the vein down dip. This allowed the mine to develop ore at the same time as it constructed the main access workings.

Small parcels of high-grade ore were sent directly to the smelter in Jerome, Arizona. In May of 1936 the mine began full operations from the 200-foot-deep inclined shaft. The mine was operated out of three levels at 85 feet, 145 feet, and 200 feet. The mine employed three miners ($3.50/day), five helpers ($3/day), one hoistman ($4/day), and one blacksmith ($3.50/day) in addition to the site manager. Operating on a single day shift, the miners would use compressed air jackhammers to break ore and waste rock from the stopes that ran off the drifts on all three levels. Helpers would sort the ore and haul it to the shaft to be hoisted out on the 1-ton capacity skip. The skip would dump ore into the 30-ton capacity ore bin on the surface. Helpers would also hand stack the waste rock as backfill in the voids left by mining operations, and install wooden stulls (roof supports). Ore pockets were reported to be irregular and made mining difficult. The mine produced 5 gallons of water per minute in the lower work-ings, and this was pumped out and stored on the surface in a 2500-gallon tank for mine use.

In June of 1936, four railcars of ore were sent to the smelter in Clarksdale (Jerome), Arizona. The next two carloads of ore went to the Octave Mine mill for processing, and later some ore was sent to the smelter in Hayden, Arizona.

By 1940 the mine was down to only three employees and mining only a small amount of ore. In a letter dated September 15, 1940, the mine manager (Dr. Hagood) reported to the board of directors that he was still having trouble with George Myers interfering with operations and would follow their instructions to "kick him off the property." The mine closed with the start of World War II. By that time, about 1000 tons of ore averaging 0.8 ounces of gold per ton had been mined. This corresponds to about 800 ounces of gold worth $28,000 in 1940 dollars. Over 800 tons of lower grade ore were reportedly left behind at the start of the war. However, almost all ore was removed from the three main levels, and the uppermost level had broken through to the surface to the west of the shaft. After the war there was little activity at the mine, and in 1947 it was offered for sale at $75,000 or for lease on a 15% royalty.

Beehive Mine

Believed by most geologists to be an extension of the Octave vein, the Beehive vein has a virtually identical mineralogy, orientation, and structure. Exceptional minerals reported and confirmed for this mine include bornite, tetrahedrite, and gold-silver tellurides. The Beehive Mine is located at the center of the Golden Age claim where the vein intersects a northwest-trending shear zone (fault).

The original owner, Mr. Zeigler, operated the mine from the late 1890s to 1915. Andrew Peterson patented the mine in 1900, and Zeigler continued to operate the mine on lease. According to reports, Zeigler met a "violent death" in 1915. In 1916 the new owner reopened the mine, built a new road, and installed new mining and milling equipment. The mine operated sporadically in the 1920s and 1930s. The Zeigler tunnel on the Golden Age claim is an inclined shaft that follows the vein down dip for 1100 feet. Various levels from the shaft had stopes on the high-grade ore. There are no detailed records of the mine workings, which are now largely under water and inaccessible. Ore pockets averaged ½ to 5 ounces of gold per ton, and one exceptionally rich ore chute yielded over 250 ounces of gold. In early 1920, Phelps Dodge Mining explored the property, and reported "pockety quartz." Unfortunately, the tonnage of ore required for a major mining operation was not blocked out, and the asking price was too high.

The mine was idle after World War II, though it has since been the subject of both serious and strange investigations. On July 31, 1980, John Elphinstone filed a report with the Arizona Division of Mines and Mineral Resources in which he claimed to have discovered high concentrations of dissolved gold in the waters of the mine. He states in the report that he would investigate a process for recovering gold from the water. Given the low solubility of gold in water, and the fact that the venture was quickly abandoned, it is highly likely that the measurements were in error or the samples had been contaminated.

In 1982, International Gold and Minerals Ltd. drilled several exploratory holes to examine the vein at depth. Results must have been at least moderately promising, as in 1984 another larger company, from Canada, began a second drilling program. Cruiser Minerals drilled several holes, and reported 4- to 8-foot-wide intercepts of the vein with depth, averaging 0.19 to 0.39 ounces of gold per ton. Though this represents a relatively high grade of ore, it just was not present in large enough tonnages to interest the big mining companies.

Hayden Mine

This mine is located on an extension of the Johnson vein and is named for the first owner, Charles Hayden. Hayden, who ran a local saloon, operated the mine from 1895 to 1901, and produced a small amount of high-grade shipping ore from a 30-foot adit and numerous small pits. When Hayden gave up on the mine in 1901, the property lay idle for almost forty years.

In a 1934 report that was filed by the owners of the mine, the remarkable claim was made that low-grade dumps on the property contain almost 30,000 tons of rock containing 30% tungsten and over 16 ounces of silver per ton. Hayden must have been an active and talented fellow to have single-handedly mined that quantity of ore from a 30-foot-deep tunnel! The silver grade of this reported "low-grade" dump greatly exceeds the grade of silver in the richest mines in the district, and to attain a level of 30% tungsten the pile would need to be composed almost entirely of tungsten minerals. Tungsten has only been reported in minor amounts in the area, notably in the Gray Fox Prospect to the northwest and the Mesa Grande Extension Prospect to the south, which are described below. These claims of tungsten at the Hayden Mine seem to be either an exaggeration or the speculation of someone who was unfamiliar with the district.

In 1938 A. V. Moore and W. Faireweather purchased the mine. A 300-foot-deep shaft was sunk on the vein, and the first parcel of ore was shipped from the mine to the smelter at Miami, Arizona, on May 31, 1939. This shipment consisted of 4,539 pounds of hand-sorted high-grade ore, and ran 4.22 ounces of gold per ton, 1.27 ounces of silver per ton, and 21% iron. After payment for shipping and smelting, there was a profit of $258. A second smaller shipment was made on July 13, 1939. This second batch of ore was only one ton, and contained 4.33 ounces of gold and 2.8 ounces of silver, with 38% iron and 0.14% copper. Profit on this second parcel was only $114. In early 1940 the shaft was blocked at the 100-foot level by a cave-in. On October 27, 1940, Moore, who claimed the ore averaged about 1/3 ounce of gold to the ton, put up the mine for sale. He also stated that the mine had a 20-foot-deep well on Antelope Creek that produced 15 gallons of water per minute, and that electric lines crossed over the property.

In 1980, Wes Rozema purchased the mine, and some minor assessment work was performed. A 1981 assay report for samples from the mine shows very low-grade gold and up to 1 ounce of silver per ton.

There are about 2050 feet of the vein exposed on the mine site, and it strikes 70° east of north, with a dip of 20° to 30° to the northwest. This quartz vein is 3 to 5 feet thick, and contains rich gold-bearing pyrite lenses similar to the more massive ore chutes at the Johnson Mine. Sections of the vein host a 1-foot-wide fault zone consisting of crushed quartz and clay. Total production from the mine was probably less than 40 ounces of gold, and 20 ounces of silver.

Laurella Mine

This small operation opened in 1907 with the sinking of a 50-foot-deep shaft. The ore from this shaft was taken to the mill at the Congress Mine. The returns on this ore were so poor that operations were suspended.

The deposit experienced renewed interest during the tough times of the Great Depression of the 1930s. G. B. Neill owned and operated the mine in the late 1930s and installed a test mill that could process 10 tons of ore per day. He also installed a gasoline generator, compressor for drills, and electric hoist for the shaft. Water for the operation was pumped from Antelope Creek. By focusing efforts on the sections of the 3-foot-thick vein that were richest in pyrite and chalcopyrite, Neill was able to mine small parcels of 2 to 3 tons that averaged ½ to 3 ounces of gold and 1 ounce of silver to the ton.

With this encouraging result, Neill had a small cabin built on the site and hired three contract miners to cut 60 feet of drifts on the vein, and stope (remove) all of the vein to the surface. A railcar containing 54 tons of this ore were shipped to the Phelps Dodge smelter in Jerome, Arizona, in February 1939. This ore only averaged ½ ounce of gold and ½ ounce of silver to the ton, yielding 27 ounces of each metal. To improve upon this disappointing result, a second parcel of 30 tons was carefully trimmed and sorted before being sent to the smelter in August 1939. This ore yielded 32 ounces of gold, and 34 ounces of silver, enough for the down payment on a small 10-ton-per-hour ball mill and cyanide plant. Unfortunately the best of the ore had already been removed, and further sporadic mining through 1941 only yielded another 25 ounces of gold. The mine was closed for good in mid-1941, and put up for sale for $15,000.

Yarnell Mine

The Yarnell deposit was discovered in the late 1800s, and by 1914 the main vein was being mined through a 160-foot-long tunnel on the Juniper claim. Other original claims include the Triangle, Edward, and Edgar. Closed in 1916, the mine was re-opened in 1936 by the Winslow Gold Mining Company with a 70-ton-per-day flotation plant. Later in 1940 this mill was upgraded to handle 125 tons per day. Mining was centered upon the 210-foot-deep Human Shaft. Levels at 75, 125, and 190 feet deep were connected by open stopes for ore removal and raises. Over 2000 feet of tunnels were excavated. Operations were suspended in 1941 with the start of World War II.

A major open pit operation was proposed in the late 1990s by BEMA Gold Corporation of Canada. Over 30,000 feet of drilling has been performed in a total of 123 reverse-circulation drill holes, and 4 diamond-drill core holes. According to company reports, the defined ore body is 7.15 million tons averaging 0.036 ounces of gold per ton, with a 0.01 ounce per ton cutoff grade. This translates to about 261,000 ounces of recoverable gold. The company proposes to mine the deposit in an open pit, using safe, modern leaching methods to recover gold. Mining is planned for six years at a rate of 1.2 million tons per year for a gold production of 33,000 ounces per year. The company is presently waiting to open operations due to low gold prices, and the laborious process of obtaining environmental and operating permits.

The veins at this site consist of quartz with gold-bearing galena, pyrite, and chalcopyrite. The veins strike 45° east of north, dip 10° to 40° to the northwest, and are up to 30 feet thick. The largest concentration of veins is cut by a shear zone.

Yellow Jacket/Rendezvous/Last Chance Mines

The Yellow Jacket, Rendezvous, and Last Chance mines are all part of a contiguous group of workings centered on a northwest-striking vein that dips shallowly to the north. The vein is bordered by andesite and diabase dikes, is up to 5 feet thick, and has been subject to significant faulting and shearing. The main vein averages less than 0.1 ounce of gold per ton, but has many high-grade ore chutes that are up to 2 ounces of gold and 6 ounces of silver per ton of ore. There are several smaller veins on the property that average 0.03 ounces of gold per ton.

The deposit was first mentioned as having been prospected and claimed in 1905. A 1917 report states that a 14-inch-wide section of the vein was galena rich and contained 13 ounces of gold to the ton, but does not discuss any mining activity. In 1939 the first significant production from the workings yielded a few tons of low-grade ore from shallow adits and prospect pits. In 1959 J. L. Riggins, Rampage, and Carter owned the site. An adit was driven on the Rendezvous claim for 165 feet, following the richer 14-inch segment of the vein. Unfortunately, the richer galena ore became scarcer as the workings advanced, and the mine was abandoned.

In the early 1980s the site received renewed attention due to unusually high gold prices. In 1980, Wayne Peters brought several high-grade samples with visible gold, silver-rich galena, pyrite, and chalcopyrite in to the Arizona Division of Mines and Mineral Resources offices. A visit to the site by an engineer of the Arizona Division of Mines and Mineral Resources in early 1981 showed that the vein was generally very low in gold and silver, though very small high-grade lenses were present. Later in 1981 a small cut was mined on a 2-foot-wide fault zone that runs through a topographic saddle above the Last Chance claim. This fault strikes 35° east of north, dips 57° to the northeast, and apparently contains only minor amounts of gold.

Golden Goose Mine

This alluvial mine was supposedly named for "goose egg" sized nuggets that were found on the property in the 1800s. Consisting of three claims of twenty acres each along Weaver Creek, the mine has three shafts (10, 14, and 20 feet deep), and five tunnels (40, 50, 60, 80, and 200 feet long). The deposit is up to 10 yards deep, and is believed to be a combination of alluvial gold, and gold from an ancient landslide off Rich Hill. This landslide is delineated by physical features and vegetation, and is about 1320 yards by 220 yards. Containing up to 90% large boulders and blocks, alluvial mining on this site is an exhaustive, expensive, and dangerous proposition.

In 1961 the mine was owned by the 1960 gold-panning championship winner, Leland "Lee" Kelley. A 1961 report states that the mine contains over 1 million cubic yards of gravels with up to 0.1 ounces of gold per cubic yard, but was nearly impossible to work by hand due to the boulders. Mechanized mining in the late 1960s met with moderate success, but most profits were consumed by the cost of moving boulders.

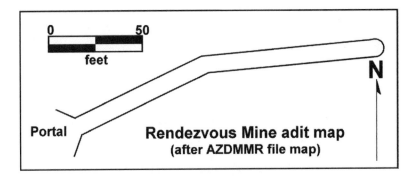

Figure E-2. Map of the main adit on the Rendezvous claim. Excavated in 1959, this tunnel is 165 feet long, and follows a weakly mineralized vein 14 inches wide.

Endependence Mine

The Endependence Mine is a play upon words that express the desire of many small mine operators: to end-dependence! This mine consists of nine claims centered upon a 2-foot-wide quartz vein that strikes northeast and dips 22° to the northwest. The vein has many small and irregular high-grade pockets of fine-grained galena that average 7 ounces of gold per ton. One remarkable "bonanza" ore pocket in 1917 reportedly yielded a ton of galena and native gold ore that produced 66 ounces of gold and 128 ounces of silver.

The mine was opened in 1913 and the vein was mined from two inclined shafts. The #1 inclined shaft was 45 feet deep, while 300 feet uphill and to the west the #2 inclined shaft reached a depth of 110 feet. Water now fills both shafts to within 20 feet of the surface. The #2 shaft was the main producer, and a horse-powered whim was used to haul ore and bail water from the mine. A 1917 report suggested replacing the horses, and stated that "it is not likely to become embarrassing if the mine is equipped with a modern pumping plant." Small surface prospect cuts are also located on the site. A three-room shack and a small blacksmith shop also were located on the property at one time.

Mesa Grande Addition

The Mesa Grande Addition is "unusual" in the Weaver District because it is not a gold mine. George W. J. Miller claimed the Mesa Grande Addition in September of 1953, and the mine produced limited amounts of tungsten between 1953 and 1958. Located just east of the windmill that bears the owner's name (Miller), and south of the Octave Mine, there are three small open cuts about 15 feet by 8 feet, and a total of 45 feet of shallow tunnels and shafts. Documented production from the workings totals 150 pounds of 74% pure tungsten oxide (WO_3). The tungsten mineral scheelite occurs in rich lenses up to 4 inches wide where fracture sets intersect a 2-foot-wide quartz vein. The fracture sets trend 70° east of north and 10° west of north, dipping 65° to 70°. The vein is oriented almost perfectly north and south, and can be traced for over 50 feet. Another vein about 75 feet to the north of the workings is 70 feet long, 4 feet wide, and has many small lenses of scheelite.

The mineral scheelite ($CaWO_4$) is often noted for being fluorescent under ultra-violet light (black light). This mineral is a pale white to gray or tan, and is easily confused with quartz during the day. If collecting scheelite by daylight, check the heft of samples, as scheelite is very dense and will feel "heavy." At night, prospecting with a portable blacklight makes the job much easier, as scheelite will glow with a faint blue fluorescence.

Approximately 150 feet east of the mine is a large body of schist that contains magnetite, ilmenite, and chromite. The unique composition and concentration of minerals within this dark rock is sufficient to deflect the needle on a compass.

Red Metal Mine

Operated by Mildred Consolidated Mining Company in the 1910s and 1920s, this deposit consists of a 3-foot-wide vein of quartz that averages ½ ounce of gold per ton and 3.3 ounces of silver per ton, with high-grade ore chutes up to 3 ounces of gold per ton. The vein was mined from a 700-foot adit and a 205-foot shaft with 110 feet of drifts. In 1920 A. V. Moore owned the mine, while Dan Genung served as mine manager. Little is known about this mine, as most records were lost when the company closed the mine.

Mizpah/Eagle Mines

The Mizpah and Eagle mines are located on a block of seven contiguous claims that host a near vertical quartz vein with very small amounts of gold-bearing pyrite. The main workings are the 500-foot-deep Eagle Shaft on the Cherokee claim, the 50-foot "old shaft," and the 560-foot Mizpah Shaft on the Alaska claim. The Mizpah Shaft is inclined at 70° and has three main levels at 200, 400, and 540 feet. The 400-foot level has several low-grade ore zones that were mined in the early 1920s to

1930s. The 540-foot level was also mined at this time, and had low-grade ore and a 6-inch-wide zone of ore averaging over 1 ounce of gold per ton. The Eagle Shaft is about 1000 feet south of the Mizpah Shaft. All workings were excavated at the turn of the century, and were later expanded by mining activity in the 1920s and 1930s.

Lucky Johnnie and Katie Mine

This was a small mine located on a vein several inches wide and 2000 feet long, and it produced less than 10 ounces of gold from about 20 tons of ore in the 1930s. The mine is located next to the Morning Star placers. Mining on this site was restricted to an open surface cut and some prospect pits.

Helen Morris Mine

Located on the Gold King and Clinton claims on the Gold King vein, this mine exploited a quartz vein that was up to 10 inches wide and dipping 30°. The vein had a minor amount of gold-bearing pyrite, and averaged 0.25 ounces of gold to the ton, with high-grade zones of 1 ounce of gold to the ton. In 1946 under the direction of the owner, Martin Standish, a crew of three men put down a 100-foot-deep inclined shaft to follow the vein. Short drifts were developed on the 50-foot level, and 15 tons of the richest ore were shipped out to pay for development costs, and 16 ounces of gold were recovered. The mine closed shortly after the ore shipment, suggesting the ore was not as rich as the owner had anticipated.

Jerome Mine

This mine is located on two claims, and consists of an inclined shaft 146 feet deep, with 4 drifts, each 18 to 36 feet long. The vein followed by the inclined shaft dips at 33° and is 1 to 4 feet thick. Frank Murphy and a man named "Gage" discovered the deposit in 1891, and mined a small amount of ore between 1892 and 1899. The property was idle from 1899 to 1940. In 1940 Luis Rahn owned the property, and attempted to revitalize the mine. Unfortunately, the outbreak of World War II loomed on the horizon, and the mine was never officially re-opened.

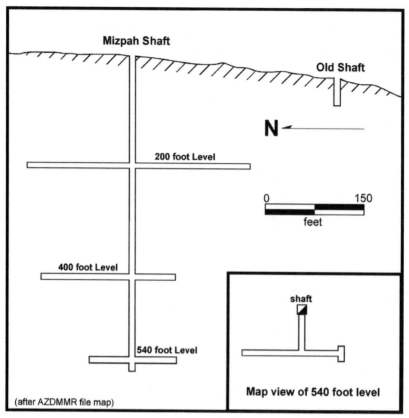

Figure E-3. Mine cross-section from September, 1921, of the Mizpah Mine.

Gray Fox Mine

The Gray Fox Mine consists of two unpatented claims that produced 180 pounds of WO_3 tungsten concentrates between 1952 and 1954. The tungsten minerals scheelite and ferberite occur as stringers and pods in a quartz vein trending 50° east of north, and dipping 65° to the southeast. The vein is hosted in a metamorphic rock (schist). Two shafts of about 20-foot depth each, and three shallow open cuts in the hill were the main workings. As with the Mesa Grande, try exploring with a battery-powered blacklight at night in the slopewash below this mine.

Pyramid Prospect

This deposit was probably originally located in the 1800s, but iron was of little interest in a district with so many rich gold prospects. This deposit, also called the Stanton Magnetite Taconite, was first mentioned in a 1942 report by the War Materials Board. The geologist, Mr. Price, concluded that the deposit was of too limited size and too low grade for production, even by wartime standards.

The deposit is located along the Stanton-Yarnell road within Yavapai Group rocks. Magnetite occurs as laminations within quartzite, greenstone, and schist. The richest of the iron formations is about 200 feet wide, and over three miles long, while lower-grade material is up to a mile wide. This formation dips nearly vertical, adding to the difficulty of ever mining the iron. "Typical" samples collected by the U.S. Bureau of Mines in 1961 averaged 25% iron, 0.3% titanium, 2% manganese, 0.2% phosphorus, 0.1% sulfur, 50% silica, and traces of cobalt, copper, nickel, and vanadium.

The deposit has never been mined, but makes for an interesting stop to examine the large blocks of banded magnetite-quartz rock. This deposit probably contributed significant quantities of black magnetite sand to Antelope Creek, which would have clogged the sluices and drywashers of the early miners.

Appendix F
Gold-Prospecting Clubs

The Lost Dutchman's Mining Association

P.O. Box 891499
Temecula, CA 92589-1449
(909) 699-4749

The Lost Dutchman's Mining Association (LDMA) was founded by George, Wilma, Perry, and Tom Massie in 1976 to provide places where men, women, and their families could meet, prospect, and mine for gold. Beginning with one historic gold property, Italian Bar in California's Mother Lode, the LDMA now has an ever-growing number of private properties and claims in several western states and also in Georgia, South Carolina, and North Carolina. Lost Dutchman's private camps and claims boast some of the finest gold reserves and prospecting in this country.

The most important consideration for evaluating new properties for the LDMA is their gold-producing potential. Exhaustive tests are made in the area to ensure that Lost Dutchman's members will have continued access to proven gold reserves. Members in the past years have reported finding some very large nuggets on the properties.

LDMA members also have access to a multitude of valuable mining claims in some of the West's richest mining areas. All of the gold that members find is theirs to keep. Members enjoy prospecting and mining seminars, demonstrations, field trips, camaraderie, and more.

Stanton is 120-patented acres of an old ghost town with several buildings dating back to the 1870s. It was first purchased by the LDMA in 1978. LDMA members can enjoy dredging and high-banking along Antelope Creek (when water is available), drywashing, coin shooting, and nugget hunting. Stanton is not open to GPAA members; however, LDMA members have access to all GPAA properties.

A membership in the LDMA can be purchased through the head office for $5,000.00, or $3,500.00 if purchased at Stanton. Maintenance fees are $120 per year. A single membership covers married couples and all children under the age of eighteen. It lasts a lifetime and can be sold or passed on to another individual.

Gold Prospector's Association of America (GPAA)

P.O. Box 891509
Temecula, CA 92589-1509
(909) 699-4749
www.goldprospectors.org

The GPAA was founded in 1968 to provide a platform for the exchange of information and to present an organized voice for recreational as well as professional prospectors and miners. Today, it is the world's largest gold-prospecting organization. The GPAA has more than 5,000 acres of mining claims available to its members, in thirty-seven U.S. states and several Canadian provinces, including the Northwest Territory. Every member receives a subscription to the *Gold Prospector* magazine. They are also entitled to two free ore evaluations each year. A lifetime membership in the GPAA can be purchased for $950, or a one-year membership can be obtained for $87.

Roadrunner Prospector's Club, Inc.

P.O. Box 56804
Phoenix, AZ 85079-6804
(602) 274-2521

The Roadrunner Prospector's Club is a nonprofit Arizona corporation, whose purpose is to foster the science and art of prospecting, and to acquire claims for the exclusive use of its members. The Roadrunners have over a thousand acres of mining claims. A lifetime membership costs $1,500. The initial fee is $20 and another $120 to receive the club badge. Dues can be handled on a monthly basis, after the initial enrollment, or payments can be made on an annual basis. The club offers a 20% discount for total payment of dues. This is a family membership, meaning it covers husband, wife, and minor children (under twenty-one). When children reach the age of twenty-one, they can join at a discount. A monthly newsletter is mailed to each member that tells the planned agenda and location of each meeting.

Arizona Association of Gold Prospectors (AAGP)

P.O. Box 35281
Phoenix, AZ 85069-5281
(623) 934-6882
http://members.nbci.com/azgoldpros

The AAGP is dedicated to providing members with monthly meetings, mining events such as outings and common digs, and great local claims to prospect on. Most of their claims are within a one- or two-hour drive from northern Phoenix, Glendale, Scottsdale, Mesa, or Tucson. The AAGP is also the only club in Arizona to offer its members year-round free access to a commercial placer gold-mining operation located at the base of Red Picacho Volcano near Wickenburg and Morristown.

Basic initial membership and annual maintenance fees cost $150.00. A maintenance fee of $110.00 is due on the first day of the annual anniversary date following the initial application. "Gold Getter" initial membership and annual maintenance fees cost $300.00. A maintenance fee of $220.00 is due on the first day of the annual anniversary date following the initial application. Members will receive an AAGP Gold Claims Guide, membership badge, and a 15% discount on all Gold King prospecting equipment.

Mesa Gold Diggers Prospecting Club

(480) 833-3378 or (480) 598-0140

A relatively small organization formed in 1984 with several claims throughout Arizona. Gold panning, dredging, drywashing, metal detecting, raffles, potlucks, treasure hunts, and weekend outings are offered. The club meets the first Tuesday or Wednesday of each month at 7:00 p.m. at the Mesa Public Library, Saguaro Room, 2nd floor, 64 E. 1st Street, Mesa, AZ 85201. Membership in the Mesa Gold Diggers Club costs $25.00, yearly renewal is $15.00.

Weaver Mining District

P.O. Box 955
Congress, AZ 85332
(520) 427-6344

Before Arizona became a state and was still a territory, Congress passed a bill allowing these territories to form mining districts and to pass laws to govern themselves. The Weaver Mining District, now based in Congress, was established in 1863.

The Weaver Mining District office is located in the old gas station, next to the Arrowhead Bar and Restaurant, two miles north of Congress on U.S. Highway 89. Dan Jacobs is chairman of the board. Les Bender and Jim Miller are joint vice-chairmen, and Norma Jones is secretary-treasurer. There are seventeen people on the board of directors.

The Weaver Mining District has a 160-acre mining claim in the Rich Hill area available for use by its members. Volunteers are usually available to answer any questions pertaining to gold mining in the Rich Hill area. Cost of a membership is $25.00.

Gold, Rock, & Gem Adventures (GRGA)

P.O. Box 26333
Prescott Valley, Arizona 86312
(877) 588-3377
www.goldrockgem.com

The GRGA is a leading full service gold, rock, gem, and fossil prospecting organization dedicated to providing its members with the very best array of outdoor experiences, and quality properties across the United States. This organization is operated by professional prospectors, mineral exploration geologists, rock hounds, and outdoor experts. Unlike many other clubs, they offer a continually expanding portfolio of tested and proven high quality properties rich in the treasures of the earth.

The GRGA currently has thousands of acres of quality mining claims and sites throughout the western United States with a strong emphasis in the goldfields of Nevada and Arizona. Properties are continually being added as their team of experts carefully evaluates each prospective property. Property identification is facilitated by exclusive access to a large mining company's records, which cover tens of thousands of potential sites.

Members will receive periodic newsletters with important updates pertaining to new property acquisitions, events, and educational articles. Each new property will be outlined in an easy to read report, with a clear, simple, detailed map to each of the claim sites. Staff members are available to answer any questions, discuss ideas and offer suggestions to improve their members' overall prospecting experiences. First year membership in the GRGA costs $150.00, yearly renewal is $125.00.

Rich Hill Gold Hunters

P.O. Box 115
Morristown, Arizona 85342
(602) 382-2632
(602) 237-2300 (fax)
rustyandbetty@hotmail.com

This new club has obtained ownership of the Devil's Nest property once owned by the 24K Club. Members will have the opportunity to prospect this historic area and enjoy activities such as gold-related workshops and seminars. The Rich Hill Gold Hunters Club is also bringing back the famous "dozer pushes". Selected areas will be excavated for the sole use of the club members. A membership can be purchased for $300 per year.

DISCLAIMER

The authors of this book are not endorsed by or solely affiliated with any of the aforementioned recreational clubs or organizations. We accept no responsibility for any injury that might incur while prospecting on club property, nor do we make any guarantees as to the amount of gold you will find or the legitimacy of the mining claims. We recommend you conduct your own research beforehand, in order to determine which gold-prospecting organization is right for you.

References and Suggested Readings

Chapter 2

Bateman, A. M. (1967). *Economic Mineral Deposits*. 2nd Edition. New York: John Wiley and Sons, 916 pp.

Boyle, R. W. (1979). "The Geochemistry of Gold and its Deposits." Geological Survey of Canada, Bulletin 280.

Boyle, R. W. (1987). *GOLD; History and Genesis of Deposits*. New York: Van Nostrand Reinhold Co., 676 pp.

Griffith, R. (2000). "The Tongue Nugget." *Gold Prospector Magazine* (July/August):1, 8–9.

Guilbert, J. M., and Park, C. F., Jr. (1986). *The Geology of Ore Deposits*. New York: W. H. Freeman and Company, 985 pp.

Heikes, V. C. (1913). "Dry Placers in Arizona." *US Geological Survey, Mineral Resources for 1912*, part I, pp. 257–259.

Jenny, J. P., and Reynolds, S. J. (1989). "Geologic Evolution of Arizona." *Arizona Geological Society Digest* 17.

Johnson, M. (1972). "Placer Gold Deposits of Arizona." US Geological Survey Bulletin 1355, pp. 60–62.

Lindgren, W. (1933). *Mineral Deposits*. New York: McGraw-Hill Company, 930 pp.

Sawyer, D. L. (1932). "Sampling a Gold Placer." *Engineering and Mining Journal* (July): 381–383.

Watson, H. B. (1918). "Rich Hill Observations." *Arizona Mining Journal*, 11, no. 7: 8–11.

Wilson, E. D. (1952). *Arizona Gold Placers and Placering*. 5th edition, revised. Arizona Bureau of Mines Mineral Technology Series no. 45, Bulletin 160, Tucson, AZ, 124 pp.

Chapter 3

Bolton, H. E., ed. (1908). *Spanish Exploration in the Southwest 1542–1706*. Original Narratives of Early American History Series. New York: Barnes & Noble, Inc.

Farish, T. E. (1915). *History of Arizona*. Phoenix, AZ: The Filmer Brothers Electrotype Company.

Hodge, F. W., and Lewis, T. H., eds. (1907). *Spanish Explorers in the Southern United States 1528–1543*. Original Narratives of Early American History Series. New York: Barnes & Noble, Inc.

Natella, A. A. (1980). *The Spanish in America 1513–1979: A Chronology and Fact Book*. Dobbs Ferry, NY: Oceana Publications, Inc.

Simmons, M. (1991). *The Last Conquistador: Juan de Onate and the Settling of the Far Southwest*. Norman and London: University of Oklahoma Press.

Walker, H. P., and Bufkin, D. (1979). *Historical Atlas of Arizona*. Norman: University of Oklahoma Press.

Chapter 4

Byrkit, J., and Hooper, B. (1993). *The Story of Pauline Weaver: Arizona's Foremost Mountain Man.* Sierra Azul Productions.

Coggin, H. M. (1987). "A History of Placer Mining in Arizona." In History of Mining in Arizona.

Farish, T. E. (1915). *History of Arizona*. Phoenix, AZ: The Filmer Brothers Electrotype Company.

Genung, D. B. (1992). *Death in His Saddlebags: Charles Baldwin Genung, Arizona Pioneer.* Manhattan, KS: Sunflower University Press.

Hall, S. M. (1929). "First Citizen of Prescott." Article from the *Arizona Republican,* April 10.

Heatwole, T. (1981). *Ghost Towns and Historical Haunts in Arizona*. Phoenix, AZ: Golden West Publishers.

Lauer, C. D. (1990). *Tales of Arizona Territory*. Phoenix, AZ: Golden West Publishers.

Lorey, F. C., III. (1999). "Gold of the Weaver Mountains." *International California Mining Journal* 68: 22–26.

Sandholdt, P. (1985). "Some Paulino Weaver Material" pp. 9. Sharlott Hall Museum.

Sherman, J. E., and Sherman, B. H. (1969). *Ghost Towns of Arizona*. Norman: University of Oklahoma Press.

Stano, M. G. (1989). "Charles Stanton." Article from the *The Nevadan Today*, March 26.

Thomas, B. (1992) "Stanton Is Named for Killer." Article from the *The Arizona Republic*, March 29.

Weight, H., and Weight, L. (1952). *Old Pauline Weaver: Frontiersman, Free Trapper, Scout, Guide, Prospector*. vol. 8, no. 3. Calico Print.

Wells, E. (1927). *Argonaut Tales: Stories of the Gold Seekers and the Indian Scouts of Early Arizona*. New York: The Grafton Press.

Wilburn, J. D. (1978). *Arizona's Rich Hill: The West's Most Amazing Gold Strike*. Lane Printing Publications.

Willson, R. (1966). "Gold Thick as Potatoes." Article from *Arizona Days and Ways*, November 27.

Young, O. E. (1967). "How They Dug the Gold: An Informal History of Frontier Prospecting, Placering, Lode-Mining, and Milling in Arizona and the Southwest." Arizona Pioneers' Historical Society.

Chapters 5-7

Anderson, P. (1989). "Stratigraphic Framework, Volcanic-Plutonic Evolution, and Vertical Deformation of the Proterozoic Volcanic Belts of Central Arizona." in J.P. Jenny and S.J. Reynolds, S.J., eds., "Geologic Evolution of Arizona." *Arizona Geological Society Digest* 17: 57–147.

Bateman, A. M. (1967). *Economic Mineral Deposits*. 2nd edition. New York: John Wiley and Sons, 916 pp.

Blake, W. P. (1899) "Report of the Territorial Geologist." In Report of the Governor of Arizona for 1899, Arizona Territorial Government, Phoenix, AZ.

Botts, G. (1995). *The Vulture–Gold Mine of the Century*. Phoenix, AZ: Quest Publishing Group, 140 pp.

Boyle, R. W. (1979). "The Geochemistry of Gold and Its Deposits." Geological Survey of Canada, Bulletin 280.

Boyle, R. W. (1987). *GOLD; History and Genesis of Deposits*. New York: Van Nostrand Reinhold Co., 676 pp.

Dale, V. B. (1959). "Tungsten Deposits of Gila, Yavapai, and Mohave Counties, Arizona." US Bureau of Mines, Informational Circular 8078.

DeWitt, E., (2001). Personal communication.

Dinsmore, C. A. (1912). "The Congress Junction Mining District, Arizona." *Mining Engineering World* 36:1006–1007.

Griffith, R. (2000). "The Tongue Nugget." *Gold Prospector Magazine* (July/August):1, 8–9.

Guilbert, J. M., and Park, C. F., Jr. (1986). *The Geology of Ore Deposits*. New York: W. H. Freeman and Company, 985 pp.

Hamilton, P. (1883). "Resources of Arizona." Arizona Division of Mines and Mineral Resources file data from a report to the territorial governor.

Heatwole, T. (1982). *Arizona–off the Beaten Path!*. Phoenix, AZ: Golden West Publishers, 142 pp.

Heikes, V. C. (1913). "Dry Placers in Arizona." *US Geological Survey, Mineral Resources for 1912*, part I, pp. 257–259.

Herald, C. E., and Russ, M. D. (1985). "Geology and Mineralization of the Congress Mine." In *Geology of the Vulture and Congress Mines, Maricopa and Yavapai Counties, Arizona*. Arizona Geological Society, 1985 Spring Field Trip Guidebook, 5 pp.

Johnson, M. (1972). "Placer Gold Deposits of Arizona." US Geological Survey Bulletin 1355, pp. 60–62.

Keith, S. B., Gest, D. E., DeWitt, E., Woode, N., and Everson, B. A. (1983). "Metallic Mineral Districts and Production in Arizona." *Arizona Bureau of Geology and Mineral Technology Bulletin* 194: 58.

Lindgren, W. (1933). *Mineral Deposits*. New York: McGraw-Hill Company, 930 pp.

Manning, R. (1989). *What is Arizona Really Like?*. Phoenix, AZ: Reganson Publishing, 120 pp.

McConnell, R. G. (1907). "Report on gold values in the Klondike high-level gravels." *Canada Geological Survey*, 34 pp.

Metzger, O. H., "Gold Mining and Milling in the Wickenburg Area, Maricopa and Yavapai Counties, Arizona." *US Bureau of Mines Information Circular 6991*, 78 pp.

Miller, M. A., Page, T. C., and Sell, J. D. (1991). "Geology and Mineralization at the Yarnell Gold Deposit, Yavapai County, Arizona." In K. E. Karlstrom, ed., "Proterozoic Geology and Ore Deposits of Arizona." *Ariz. Geological Society Digest* 19: 301–308.

Nevius, J. N. (1921). "Resuscitation of the Octave Gold Mine." *Mining and Scientific Press* 123: 122–124.

Niemuth, N. (2001). Personal communication.

Sawyer, D. L. (1932). "Sampling a Gold Placer." *Engineering and Mining Journal* (July): 381–383.

Shaw, S. F. (1909). "Operation and Production of the Congress Mines." *Mining World* 30: 387–388.

Staunton, W. F. (1926). "Ore Possibilities at the Congress Mine." *Engineering and Mining Journal* 122: 769–771.

Trimble, M. (1982). *Arizona Adventure*. Phoenix, AZ: Golden West Publishers, 160 pp.

Watson, H. B. (1918). "Rich Hill Observations." *Arizona Mining Journal* 11, no. 7: 8–11.

Watson, H. B. (1918). "Rich Hill Observations." *Arizona Mining Journal* 2: 8–10.

Wilson, E. D. (1938). "Some Arizona ore deposits–Octave Mine." Arizona Bureau of Mines, Geological Series no. 12, Bulletin 145, pp. 130–132.

Wilson, E. D. (1952). *Arizona Gold Placers and Placering*, 5th edition, revised, Arizona Bureau of Mines Mineral Technology Series no. 45, Bulletin 160, Tucson, AZ, 124 pp.

Wolle, M. S. (1955). *The Bonanza Trail–Ghost Towns and Mining Camps of the West.* Bloomington: Indiana University Press, 510 pp.

Chapter 8

Lyman, Fred. (2001). Personal Interview on file at Sharlot Hall Museum. January 30.

Thomason, Clyde. (2000). Personal Interview on file at Sharlot Hall Museum. December 14.

Thomason, Clyde. (2001). Personal Interview on file at Sharlot Hall Museum, January 30.

Warner, Virginia. (2001). Personal Interview on file at Sharlot Hall Museum, February 8.

Chapter 9

Article on the Arizona Patriots, www.nizkor.org.

Hall, A. (1986). "Covert Probe of Right-Wing Group Brings Arrests, Foils Robbery Plot." Article from the *Arizona Republic*, December 16.

Hall, A. (1986). "'Patriots' Group Called 'Cavemen with Bombs'." Article from the *Arizona Republic*, December 17.

(1980). "Suspect in Alleged $7 Million Gold Stock Swindle Arrested." Article from the *Western Prospector and Miner*, March.

Thomas, R. L. (1977). "Feud bristles with pistols." Article from the *Arizona Republic*, February 13.

Wayman, K. (1977). "Octave Preacher to Fight Dismissal of Gun Charge." Article from the the *Arizona Republic*, April 2.

Wilson, M. (1979). "Thar's Still Gold in Them Thar Hills." Article from the *Arizona Republic*, April 8.

Chapter 10 and Appendix B

Driscoll, Ronald W. (2000) Personal Interview, December 18.

Straight, J. (1988). *Nuggetshooting Dryplacer Areas/ Follow the Drywashers*. California: RDK/Advance Graphics. pp. 14–15.

Gholson, C. (1998). *Metal Detecting for Placer Gold/ A Simple Guide to Finding Gold with a Metal Detector*. Glendale, AZ: Capital Litho. pp. 48.

Johnson, M. G. (1987). *Placer Gold Deposits of Arizona*. California: Gem Guides Book Company.

Klauber, L. M. (1982). *Rattlesnakes/ Their Habits, Life Histories, & Influence on Mankind*. Berkley, CA: University of California Press.

Straight, J. (1996). *Advanced Prospecting & Detecting for Hardrock Gold*. California: Jim Straight.

Wilson, E. D. (1933). *Arizona Gold Placers and Placering*. Arizona Bureau of Mines, No. 35, Bulletin No. 135. California: Gem Guides Book Company.

Appendix C

American Academy of Orthopedic Surgeons. (1981). *Emergency care and transportation of the sick and injured*. Chicago, IL: AAOS.

American Red Cross. (1979). *Advanced first aid and emergency care*. Garden City, NY: Doubleday Press.

Angier, B. (1974). *Survival with Style; in Trouble or in Fun...How to Keep the Body and Soul Together in the Wilderness*. New York: Vintage Books.

Bowman, W. (1988). *Outdoor Emergency Care: Comprehensive First Aid for Non-urban Settings*. Denver, CO: National Ski Patrol.

Brown, T. (1983). *Tom Brown's Field Guide to Wilderness Survival.* New York: Morgan Press.

Carr, W. (1947). *Desert Parade: A Guide to Southwestern Desert Plants and Wildlife.* New York: Viking Press.

Erven, L. (1976). *Handbook of Emergency Care and Rescue.* Beverly Hills, CA: Glencoe Press.

Greenberg, M. (1989). *Emergency Care: Medical and Trauma Scenarios.* Philadelphia: Lippincott.

Howes, P. (1954). *The Giant Cactus Forest and Its World: A Brief Biology of the Giant Cactus Forests of our American Southwest.* New York: Duell, Sloan, and Pearce.

Jaeger, E. (1961). *Desert wildlife.* Stanford, CA: Stanford University Press.

Kaston, B. and Kaston, E. (1953). *How to Know the Spiders: Picture-keys for Determining the More Common Spiders.* Dubuque, IA: W. C. Brown Co.

Klauber, L. (1982). *Rattlesnakes and Their Habits, Life Histories, and Influence on Mankind.* Berkeley, CA: University of California Press.

Manning, R. (1969). *What Kinda Cactus Izzat?.* Phoenix, AZ: Reganson Books.

Preston-Mafham, R. (1996). *The Book of Spiders and Scorpions.* New York: Barnes and Noble Books.

Sheehy, S. (1990). *Manual of Emergency Care.* St. Louis, MO: Mosby Press.

Wagner, F. (1980). *Wildlife of the Deserts.* New York: Abrams.

Wiewandt, T. (1990). *The Hidden Life of the Desert.* New York: Crown Publishers.

Wright, A. (1957). *Handbook of Snakes of the United States and Canada.* Ithaca, NY: Comstock Publishing Assocciates.

Appendix D

Clemens, S. L. (1872). *Roughing It*. 1982 reprint from the 1872 first edition, Hartford, CT: Time-Life Books, Inc.

Index

Symbols

24K Club 145, 146, 148, 150
  brochure 147, 149
  photograph 146, 149

A

Allen, Bruce G. 99, 125, 126, 132
Allen, Floyd 150
amalgamation 21, 62, 68, 69, 70, 77, 89, 90, 92, 162
amalgamation pan 62
American Smelting and Refining Company (ASARCO) 81, 83
Anonymous bearded prospector 133
Antelope Creek 23, 39, 103, 117, 134, 201, 202, 209
Antelope Mountain 39
Antelope Spring 81
Antelope Station 40, 48, 51, 52, 54
arastra 62, 63, 70, 89
Argonne National Laboratory 126
Arizona Association of Gold Prospectors (AAGP) 212
Arizona Corporation Commission 132
Arizona Division of Mines and Mineral Resources 99, 197, 200, 204
Arizona Eastern Gold Mining Company 81
Arizona Miner 59
Arizona Patriots 134, 135
Arizona State Land Department 196
Automatic Ground Tracking (AGT) 144
AZ Bureau of Geology and Mineral Technology 132

B

Babbitt, Governor Bruce 135
Basin and Range Event 20
  illustration 20
Bell, Professor Alexander Graham 137, 138
Beltrán, Friar Bernaldino 29
BEMA Gold Corporation 203
Bender, Les 213
Benton, Senator Thomas Hart 35
black widow spiders 193
Blankenship, Deputy Bill 55
Broadway, Sheriff 59
Brown, Douglas 53

C

Calderwood, Captain Martin 55
Cardenas, Don Garcia Lopez de 28
Carleton, Colonel James H. 37, 38
Carlson, Carl O. 100, 128, 130, 133
Carson, Kit 35
Casa Grande Ruins 33
  P Weaver inscription 33
  photograph 33
Caswell, Roy 134
centipedes 193
Chaney, Wallace Eugene 100, 125, 132
Cibola 26, 28, 29
Civil War 37
  Battle of Picacho Pass 38
  The Arizona Volunteers 38
claims 195
CMC Corporation 128
coil control 173
coils 181
Compass Electronics 143, 144
Conlee, T.A. 89
Consolidated Mining and Development Company 198
copper 1, 18, 162
Coronado, Francisco Vazquez de 26, 28, 29
Cortés, Hernán 25, 26
Cruiser Minerals 200
cyanidation 69, 77, 94, 162

D

Decision Corner 103, 115
dehydration 189
diabase dikes 16, 17, 203
  illustration 16
digging a target 177
Distillate Storage Company 107
donkey races 109
dozer pushing 146, 214
dredging 146
drift mining 160
Driscoll, Kathleen 145
Driscoll, Ron 143, 145, 148
drywasher 103, 104, 154, 156, 159, 163, 164
  photograph 164, 165
drywasher tailings 103, 156, 165
  photograph 156
drywashing 102, 103, 146, 163
Dunham, Elvian Sarah 119
Dunham, Matlida and Clarence 119
dynamite 65

E

Eastman Kodak Company 122
Edison, Thomas A. 163
El Paso Mountains (CA) 142
Electron Microprobe 18
   analysis 86
Elphinstone, John 200
Espejo, Antonio de 29, 30, 31
Esteban 26

F

Faireweather, W. 201
Farfán, Captain Marcos 30, 31
Favour, Alpheus H. 43
FBI 135
Fernandez, M.A. 125
Fisher, Dr. Gerhard R. 138, 139
Fisher Research Laboratory 139, 142, 143
Flores, Conchetta 118
Fort Lincoln 41, 43
Fort Whipple 41
Fosnot, David 129
   photograph 133
Fosnot, Steve 129
   photograph 133
Foster, Anne 108, 109
Foster's Ulcer Gulch 109
Frederickson, Mr. 99

G

gallium 126
Galloway, Bill 91
Galloway, Dave 91
gangue 157
Garfield, President James A. 137, 138
Gaulindo, Josepha 45
Genung, Charles 51, 52, 54, 55, 56, 59
   photograph 58
Genung, Dan 54, 206
Genung, Frank 54
Genung, Ida 51, 55
   portrait 57
geologic units
   alluvial fan 22, 23
   Apache Diabase Dikes 16, 17, 86
   Rich Hill Granites 14
   Yavapai Metamorphics 15, 17
Gibbs, H.C. 79
Gila monsters 194

226

Gilbert, Alyssa
  photograph 167
Gillick, Frank "2-gun" 114, 198
gold
  deposits
    illustration 21
  discovered at Gila City 37
  discovered at La Paz 37
  discovery at Rich Hill 39
  fire-assays 17
  industrial applications 2
  melting point 1
  nuggets
    Table 141
  purity
    mechanism for increasing 21
  total global production 1
Gold Prospector's Association of America (GPAA) 154, 211
Gold, Rock, & Gem Adventures (GRGA) 213
Grand Canyon 28
granite 1, 14, 15, 20, 22, 110, 120, 145, 154
  illustration 15
  photograph 13
  riffles 20
    illustration 19
Grant, Wilbur H. 79
Great Depression 60, 61, 102, 108, 115, 121, 202
Green, Clinton M.T. 125
greenstone 14, 15
ground balancing 171
Guiteau, Charles 137
Guzman, Nuño de 26, 28

H

Hagood, Dr. E.C. 198, 199
Hale, Vivian 99
Hallelujah Boys 127, 128, 130, 131, 133
Hallelujah Fruit Company 126
Hamilton family 89
Hancock, Judge James 131
handstacking 156, 160
Harris, W. H. 163
Hassayampa River 20, 38, 41, 105
Hastings, Marie Belle 117
Hayden, Charles 201
Hayes, Mr. and Mrs. Al 109
Haynes, Al 129
heat stroke 189
Hernandez, Elano 55, 56
Hibbert, Don C. 97, 98

highbanking 146
hot rocks 174
Hunter, Captain Sherod 38
Hunter, Thomas G. 95
hypothermia 190

I

International Gold and Minerals Ltd. 200
iridium 126
IRS 136

J

J. Walter Thompson Agency 108
J.L. Riggins, Rampage, and Carter 204
jack drilling 63, 79
   photograph 64
Jackpot Mining Co. 100
Johnson, George A.
   steamboat exploration of the Colorado 37
Johnson Gold Mines Inc. 89
Johnson, William 88, 89
   signature 89
Jones, Norma 213

K

Kearny, Colonel Stephen Watts 35
Kelland, Clarence Budington 108
Kelley, Leland "Lee" 204

L

Lambertson 46
Laramide Orogeny 19
   illustration 18
Larue, Sheriff Jody 133
lead 162
Leas, Donald S. 79
Lee, J. H. 43
Lieus, Manuel 123
Los Suertes Mining Corporation 93
Lost Dutchman's Mining Association (LDMA) 134, 154, 210
Lovett, J.C. 98
Lucero brothers 59, 112, 123
Lucero, Chano 113
Lucero, Froilano 54
Lucero, Pedro 55
Lucero, Sesto 56
Lucero, Vincente 113
Lyman, Fred 111, 122, 123, 124
   photograph 122

Lynx Creek Dredging Company 120

M

M-Scope 139
  photograph 139
MacMillan Oil Company 90
Martin, Barney 52, 53, 55
Martin massacre 55, 56, 59
Martinez District 198
Massie, George 210
Massie, Perry 210
Massie, Tom 210
Massie, Wilma 210
Maximillion, Mr. 93
May, Dennis 50, 51, 92, 93
McVeigh, Timothy 136
Mead, George 146
Mesa Gold Diggers Prospecting Club 212
metal detecting 146, 166
metal detector 157, 159
  660 Mother Lode 142
  A2B 142
  American Gold Striker 144
  Au 2000 144
  Au 52 144
  beat frequency oscillator (BFO) 139, 140, 143
  choosing 166
  Coinmaster 4900/D (49'er) 142
  Compass Challenger 143
  Diablo Gold Demon 144
  Diablo II Gold Demon 144
  first 139
  Fisher Gold Bug 143, 145
  Fisher Gold Bug II 150
  FT 16000 Fast Tracker 144
  GM 3 150
  GM 4/b 150
  Gold Scanner 143
  Goldmaster GMT 152
  Goldmaster II 144
  GP extreme 152
  Groundhog 142
  GT 16000 Ground Tracker 143, 144
  Lobo 144
  multi-period sensing (MPS) 150, 151
  pulse induction (PI) 140
  Scorpion Gold Stinger 150
  SD 2100 151, 152
  SD 2200D 151, 152
  Super Detector 150

Super Detector 2000 150
tips for use at Rich Hill 154
transmit-receive (TR) 140, 143
very low frequency (VLF) 140, 142, 143, 146, 150
XT 17000 Extra Tracker 144
Metallascope 139
meteorites 174
Mexican-American war 35
Mildred Consolidated Mining Company 206
Miller, George W. J. 205
Miller, Jim 213
Miller, Mr. 79
mine dump 68, 156, 158
photograph 158
Minelab Electronics 143, 144, 150, 151, 152
minerals
biotite 16
bismuth 18, 162
calcite 16
chalcopyrite 17, 19, 86, 93, 159, 162, 202, 203
chlorite 16
electrum 17, 162
feldspar 15, 22
ferberite 208
galena 17, 18, 68, 70, 86, 90, 92, 93, 94, 95, 159, 162, 203, 204
hematite 172
lepidocrocite 172
limonite 172
maghemite 172
magnetite 172, 209
mica 15
petzite 18
pyrite 17, 18, 19, 21, 22, 68, 70, 86, 90, 92, 94, 95, 159, 162, 202, 203, 207
quartz 15, 17, 18, 19, 21, 23, 40, 61, 86, 88, 92, 95, 203, 207, 208
scheelite 206, 208
sericite 88
silver iodide 17, 88
silver sulfate 17
silver sulfide 17, 88
sphalerite 17, 92
tellurides 162
tungsten 201
tungsten oxide 206, 208
mines
16-to-1 100, 125, 132
map 100
Beehive 149, 200
Congress 18, 50, 92, 198, 202
Devil's Nest 98
Dixie-Rincon 63, 95
map 96

Endependence 205
Golden Goose 204
Gray Fox 201, 208
Hayden 201
Helen Morris 161, 207
Jerome 207
Johnson 64, 70, 88, 89, 92, 93, 202
    map 91
Laurella 202
Leviathan 92
locator map 73
locator table 72
Lucky Johnnie and Katie 207
Lyman 124
Marcus 95, 198
Mesa Grande Extension 201, 205
Mizpah/Eagle 206
Mountainside 94
Myers 93, 112, 115, 198
Octave 17, 18, 60, 63, 65, 70, 77, 79, 83, 86, 99, 103, 106, 107, 117, 119, 121, 123, 124, 125, 126, 127, 128, 129, 131, 132, 134, 161, 162, 199, 200, 206
    geology 86
    Joker Fault 78, 79, 80
    Joker Shaft 79, 80, 81, 86
    map 80, 85
    New York Stope 80
    photograph 76, 77, 78, 81, 82, 83, 84
    production 77, 81, 85
Oro Grande 107
Planet Saturn 161
Pyramid Prospect 209
Red Metal 206
Rincon 18, 52, 120
Russell 91
Vulture 39, 49, 50, 51, 63, 92, 93
War Eagle 198
Yarnell 17, 106, 203
Yellow Jacket/Rendezvous/Last Chance 203
Montezuma 25
Moore, A.V. 116, 201, 206
Mormon Battalion 35, 37
Muller, William F. 125
Mulvernon, Sheriff 56
Murphy, 'Clubfoot' 53
Murphy, Frank 207
Murphy, Sheriff 54
Myers, George 112, 198, 199

N

Native Americans
  Apache 30, 33, 35, 38, 39, 41, 43, 46
  Aztec 25
  Hopi 28
  Moqui 29
  Weaver peace treaty 38
  Yaqui 48, 119
  Yavapai 25, 30, 38
Neill, G. B. 202
Nevius, J. Nelson 79, 80, 86
New West Prospectors Club 145
Niza, Marcos de 26, 28

O

Octave Gold Mining Company 70
  company scrip 77
Octave Mines Company, The 79
Octave School 110, 122
Octave, town of 77, 107, 110, 111, 117, 118, 119, 120, 127, 133
  photograph 48, 113
oldtimers 154, 156, 160, 165, 175, 184
Oliphant, Reverend Jack M. 126, 127, 128, 129, 130, 131, 134, 135, 136
  photograph 127, 130, 131
Oñate, Juan de 30, 31
Oro Fino Gulch 105

P

palladium 99, 126
panning 146
Partridge, William 48, 49, 51, 52
patented claims
  "400" 99
  Alaska 206
  Cherokee 206
  Chester 92
  Clinton 207
  Commodore 89
  Denver 92
  Devil's Nest 98, 112, 145, 161
  Edgar 203
  Edward 203
  Germanic 92
  Gold King 207
  Golden Age 200
  Golden Mountainside 94
  Grantly 92
  Homestake 89
  Johnson 89

Juniper 203
Last Chance 204
Leviathan 50, 51, 64, 88, 92, 93
Lucky Linda 154
Lucky Roxie 99
Mamie 94
Mountaineer 94
Mountaintop 94
Northend 94
Pick'em Up 154
Rendezvous 204
  map 205
Rock House 99
table 75
Thunderbird 105
Triangle 203
Wild Horse 99
Paul, Ed 98
pay dirt 103
pay streaks 23
Pearl Harbor 105
Peeples, Abraham Harlow 2, 38, 39, 40
Peeples Valley 49, 51, 52, 55
Pete Creek 119
Peters, Wayne 204
Peterson, Andrew 200
Phelps Dodge 98, 200, 202
Pierson, Dr. John 49, 54
pinpointing 176
placers
  alluvial 21
  eluvial 21, 22
  formation 20
  illustration 24
  La Paz 37
  paleo 23
  Red 22, 23, 98, 103, 161
  young 23
platinum 99, 126
Polk, President James K. 35
Potato Patch 2, 20, 21, 22, 114, 115, 123, 156
  discovery of 39
  formation 20
  gold purity 162
  nuggets
    purity 21
Precious Metals Mining Company 91, 92
Price, Floyd 123

R

Rahn, Luis 207
Ranch Challenge Hallelujah People 126
Ranking, Jim 123
rattlesnakes 170, 192
Redondo, Don Jose M. 37
Reval, Juan 53, 54
Reynolds Electric 118
rhenium 126
Rhenium Corporation 125, 126, 127, 131, 134
Rich, Chase 93
Rich Hill Gold Hunters 214
Rickwalt, Leo 198
Ridpath, John Clark 138
Right, Mary E. 118
Rincon Gold Mining Company 95
Rincon Holdings Company 98
Roadrunner Prospector's Club 211
Roberts, Jesse 129, 130
    photograph 129
Rodríguez, Fray Agustín 29
Rogers, Captain John 32
Rosenblatt, Judge Paul 135
Rozema, Wes 201
Russell, E.G. 91
Russell, Frank 91

S

Sanborn, Maurine 95, 107, 108
    photograph 108
Saturday Evening Post 108
scanning electron microscopy 162
Schleisman, Mr. 100
Schoonover, Henry "Buck" 100, 113, 114
scorpions 193
Segna, William 112
Seven Cities of Gold 26, 28
Sharlot Hall Museum 88
Sierra Azul, legend of 31, 38
Simmons, Rocko 129
    photograph 132
Slack and Arnold diamond mine hoax 49, 51
Smith, J.W. 89
Smith, W. B. 98
sonic boom 108
Spanish exploration
    map 27
    mines 29, 30
Spear, George 97

specific gravity
  gold 1
  lead 1
  water 1
specimen gold 61
Spurlock, Robert 111
Stainbrook, Andrew 46, 47
Stainbrook, Mrs. 46, 47
Stallings, John 131
stamp mill 63, 67
Standard Oil 107
Standish, Martin 207
Stanton, Charles P. 49, 50, 51, 52, 53, 54, 55, 56, 59, 88, 92, 93, 112, 125, 128, 154
  murder of 59
  photograph 53, 56
  Record of Naturalization 50
  signature 54
Stanton, town of 38, 52, 107, 108, 109, 111, 118, 134, 153, 154, 210
  photograph 153
stope mining 65, 89
  illustration 66
Straight, Jim 143
  photograph 139
Sunrise Bar and Dance Hall 117
Sweeney, Jim 99, 100
Swilling, Jack 39

T

tailings 68, 69
tarantulas 194
Tejo 26
Tesoro Company 144
"The Secret of Sidewinder Gulch" 108
Thomason, Amilia 118
Thomason, Belle 118
Thomason, Clyde
    99, 110, 111, 112, 113, 114, 115, 117, 120, 121, 122, 123, 124, 128, 130, 133
  photograph 110
Thomason, Earl 98, 120
Thomason, Earnest 121
Thomason, George 99
Thomason, George Washington 118, 120
Thomason, Julius Augustus 118
Thomason, Julius Augustus Jr. 118
Thomason, Julius Francis 118
Thomason, Lena 118
Thomason, Lucille 122, 123
Thrasher, George 46, 47
Timmerman, John 52, 53, 54, 88
  murder of 53

Tongue Nugget 151
Tovar, Don Pedro de 28
Tusayan 28

U

U.S. Vanadium 117
Ulcer Gulch 108, 109
Union Rock Company 121
Universal Placer Mining Corporation 105
Upton, George 94, 107, 108
Upton Oil Company 107

V

Vega, Francisco 47, 48, 51, 52, 54, 55, 59
Vega gang 52, 53, 54, 55, 56
Velásquez, Diego 25

W

Walker, Joseph R. 39
Walnut Grove 41, 44, 55, 59
Walton, Larry 153
Walton, Linda 153
War Production Board-Law-208 106, 107
Weaver, Ben 40, 41
Weaver Cemetery 117
Weaver Creek 23, 39, 86, 98, 103, 111, 119, 120, 204
Weaver Creek Saloon 112
Weaver Mining District #1 2, 37, 38
Weaver Mining District #2 40, 60, 65, 70, 195, 213
    character of the gold 161
    lode deposits 60
    placer gold production 60
Weaver Mountains 22, 40, 79, 113
    formation 20
Weaver, Pauline 32, 33, 35, 37, 39, 40
    death of 41
    discovery of La Paz placers 37
    map of exploration 34
    monument 42, 43
    obituary 42
    portrait 36
Weaver, Raymond Duff 33
Weaver, town of 40, 41, 46, 48, 51, 52, 54, 56, 112
Weaverville 40
Wells Fargo 54, 125, 135
Wells, Judge Edmund 43
White, Sexton 49, 51, 92, 93
White's Electronics 142, 144, 150, 152
Wickenburg, Henry 38, 39

Wilfley table 67, 68
Wilson, George 'Yaqui' 48, 49, 51, 52
Winslow Gold Mining Company 203
Wittliff, Al 95
World War II 83, 91, 93, 98, 105, 108, 139, 158, 199, 200, 203, 207

Y

Yarnell 40
Yavapai Mining Company 100
York, Pete Angus 119
Young, Ewing 33, 34, 38

Z

Zeigler, Mr. 200
Zuni
    village of 29, 30, 33

Dr. M. Katherine Crombie was bit by the "gold bug" on her first prospecting trip three years ago, when she specked a nice quartz-gold specimen from a wash near Rich Hill. Kate is no stranger to field work and has been involved in studies of the Adirondack Mountains, Egypt's southwestern desert, and the lead mining districts of southeastern Missouri. She is an expert in the interpretation of satellite imagery and its usefulness for variety of geologic purposes. She holds a B.S. in Geology and Television Production from Syracuse University and a Ph.D. in Earth and Planetary Sciences from Washington University in St. Louis. Kate is currently mining data for the Mars Odyssey Gamma Ray Spectrometry team at the University of Arizona.

Chris Gholson's introduction to gold prospecting started off at a very early age when his grandfather began taking him along on his many excursions into the Arizona desert to search for Indian artifacts, relics, and, of course, gold. That was nearly 20 years ago, but Chris's desire to chase the elusive metal is still alive and well. In 1998 he wrote his first book *Metal Detecting for Placer Gold*, which has sold over 3,000 copies. He is a contributing author for several magazines including the *Gold Prospector*, the *International California Mining Journal*, and *Lost Treasure*. Chris has

made several appearances on the Outdoor Channel with Perry Massie and has been featured in numerous television commercials for Minelab Electronics. In May 2000, he graduated from Arizona State University with a B.S. in the Biological Sciences. He has prospected throughout the western United States, the goldfields of Alaska, the rainforests of South America and the Australian Outback. The Arizona prospector has found numerous pounds of nuggets, handfuls of gold-bearing specimens, two rich veins in the Northern Territory of Australia, and an assortment of meteorites with his metal detector. To contact Chris please visit his website www.arizonaoutback.com

Dr. Dante Lauretta is an Assistant Professor of Cosmochemistry in the Department of Planetary Sciences at the University of Arizona. He spends most of his time analyzing the chemistry and mineralogy of meteorites in his laboratory. He first visited Stanton, Arizona, in 1977 on a ghost-town expedition with his parents. Dante became interested in the mineralization and history of the area when one of his students (Chris Gholson) asked why he always found gold nuggets in red soil. After initial skepticism, Dante became a believer when Chris brought a sack full of beautiful gold nuggets to the next class period. Dante has a B.S. in Mathematics and Physics and a B.A. in Oriental Studies from the University of Arizona. He earned his Ph.D. in Earth and Planetary Sciences from Washington University in St. Louis, where he met two of the co-authors of this book. He eventually married one of them.

Dr. Erik Melchiorre first panned gold at scout camp on the north fork of the Stanislaus River in California in 1979. For four summers on camp staff, he spent weekends cleaning out the sluice-like corrugated drainpipe under roads of the area.

Erik holds a B.S. degree in Geology from the University of Southern California, a Masters degree in Geology from Arizona State University, and a Ph.D. in Earth and Planetary Sciences from Washington University in St. Louis. He has worked at two copper mines in Arizona and is presently an Assistant Professor of Geology at California State University–San Bernardino. Erik's research focuses on the geochemistry of copper and gold deposits and the hydrology of rivers. He also has expertise in fire assay techniques. Erik is a recreational gold prospector, has found gold on three continents, and has visited over 75 gold districts and mines in the United States, Australia, Fiji, and Central America.

Rich Hill

The History of Arizona's Most Amazing Gold District

M. Katherine Crombie, Ph.D.
Chris T. Gholson, B.S.
Dante S. Lauretta, Ph.D.
Erik B. Melchiorre, Ph.D.

Read about the fascinating history of Stanton, Octave, and Weaver, three of Arizona's most notorious ghost towns

Learn about the geologic events that produced the enormous gold nuggets of Arizona's Rich Hill, including the famous Tongue Nugget

Get tips and advice on gold recovery from one of the world's premier gold prospectors

Explore detailed maps and satellite images of the mines and placer deposits around Stanton

$24.95 + $3.95 s&h

To order call
1-866-369-2468 (toll free)
or (303) 449-5995

or send money order for $28.90 to
bLogistics/Rich Hill
5757 Arapahoe Ave., Unit D-2
Boulder, CO 80303
(sorry, no checks accepted)